Investiga Station

Learning Center Projects for Investigation

Written by **Gayle Bittinger**
Illustrated by **Marilyn Barr**

Totline® Publications
A Division of Frank Schaffer Publications, Inc.
Torrance, California

Managing Editor: Kathleen Cubley
Contributing Editors: Carol Gnojewski, Susan Hodges,
   Elizabeth McKinnon, Jean Warren
Copyeditor: Kris Fulsaas
Proofreader: Miriam Bulmer
Editorial Assistant: Durby Peterson
Graphic Designer: Sarah Ness
Graphic Designer (Cover): Brenda Mann Harrison
Production Manager: Melody Olney

ISBN: 1-57029-190-X

Library of Congress Catalog Number 97-62535
Printed in the United States of America
Published by Totline® Publications
Editorial Office: P.O. Box 2250
                  Everett, WA 98203
Business Office: 23740 Hawthorne Blvd.
                  Torrance, CA 90505

20 19 18 17 16 15 14 13 12 11 10 9 8 7 6 5 4 3 2 1

Introduction

Working at stations or learning centers is a great way to introduce your children to new concepts, reinforce concepts already learned, practice skills, and have fun while learning. Station work also gives them opportunities to work independently, to remember and follow directions, and to complete projects—important skills for future learning.

The stations in this book, *Investigation Station,* provide opportunities for your children to explore and learn about the world around them. The chapters address science topics such as nature, water and air, the body and the senses, and more.

Each station project includes an objective for the lesson, a list of materials needed, directions for setting up the station, introductory information, step-by-step instructions for completing the project, and a teacher-directed follow-up. There are also reproducible worksheets and patterns to make the preparation of each station quick and easy.

Most of the activities have been written as if one child at a time were working in a station. If you are planning to have more than one child working, simply adjust the materials as needed. You may also want to have an adult helper available to assist any child who needs extra guidance.

Help your children put on their thinking caps with the easy-to-set-up stations and unique reproducible pages in *Investigation Station.*

Contents

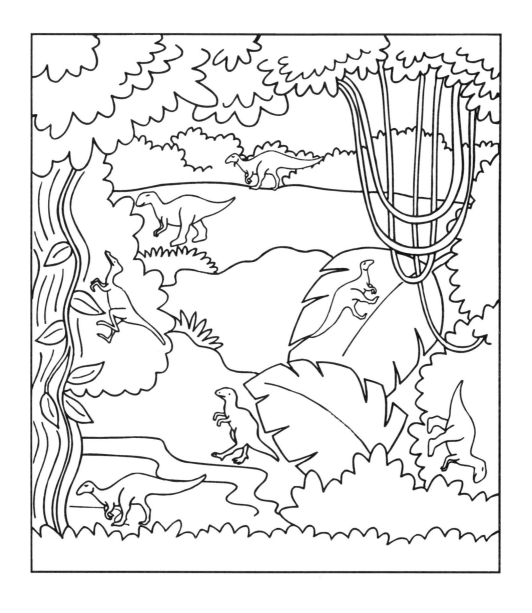

Investigating Nature

Sorting Leaves

Objectives

Practice observation and sorting skills.

Materials Needed

❑ colorful fall leaves
❑ basket
❑ construction paper

Setting Up the Station

- Collect a variety of colorful fall leaves.
- Put the leaves in a basket.
- Find construction paper in each of the fall colors represented by the leaves (orange, red, brown, yellow, etc.).
- Set out the basket of leaves and the construction paper.

Introducing the Project

Show your children several fall leaves. Ask the children to describe the leaves' colors, sizes, and shapes. Let them help you sort the leaves by shape or size or color. Then explain the following steps to your children.

The Project

1. Spread the construction paper on the table and take the leaves out of the basket.

2. Sort the leaves by placing them on the matching color of construction paper. Count how many of each color you have.

3. Think of another way to sort the leaves (size, shape, stem or no stem, etc.) and sort the leaves in that way.

4. Put the leaves back in the basket and put away the construction paper.

Follow-Up

Let the children help you create a display of fall leaves on another table or a bulletin board. Copy the worksheets on pages 9-11 for your children to work on in class or at home.

Name_____

Color the leaves orange.
Color the leaves red.
Color the leaves yellow.

Name_____

In each row, put an X over the leaf that does not match.

Name_____

In each box, circle the biggest leaf.

In each box, circle the smallest leaf.

Investigating Nature • Investigation Station **11**

Pumpkin Fun

Objectives

Practice observation skills and learn about the parts of a pumpkin.

Materials Needed

❑ pumpkins
❑ newspaper
❑ sharp knife
❑ spoon
❑ bowls
❑ sink or dishpan

Setting Up the Station

• Collect four pumpkins.
• Spread newspaper out on a table.
• Prepare the pumpkins by leaving one as is; cutting another in half; cutting the top off another; and cutting off the top and cleaning the pulp out of the last one, putting the pumpkin pulp (seeds and all) in a bowl.
• Set out all four pumpkins, the bowl of pumpkin pulp, an empty bowl, and a spoon.
• Be sure a sink or dishpan is available for hand washing.

Introducing the Project

Show your children the whole pumpkin. Talk about how pumpkins grow from seeds. Show them a pumpkin seed. Where did it come from? Let them tell you about the different ways they use pumpkins (in a pie, to make a jack-o'-lantern, etc.). Tell the children they will be exploring pumpkins today, then explain the following steps.

The Project

1. Look at the whole pumpkin. Feel the outside of the pumpkin. Lift it up. Is it heavy or light?

2. Look at the pumpkin cut in half. How is the inside different from the outside?

3. Reach into the pumpkin with the top removed. What does it feel like?

4. Look at the scooped-out pumpkin and the pumpkin pulp in the bowl. Where are the seeds?

5. Remove some of the seeds from the pumpkin pulp and place them in the seed bowl.

6. Wash your hands.

Follow-Up

Show your children the bowl of pumpkin seeds. Let them help you remove the pumpkin seeds from the other three pumpkins. Wash and bake the pumpkin seeds to eat in class. (Recipe follows.) Copy the worksheets on pages 13-15 for the children to complete in class or at home.

Roasted Pumpkin Seeds—Spread pumpkin seeds on a baking sheet and bake at 350°F for 15 minutes. Coat seeds with melted butter, Worcestershire sauce, and salt to taste. Bake at 275°F for an additional 1½ to 2 hours, stirring every 30 minutes.

Name_____

Find the pumpkins and color them orange.

Name_____

Cut out the boxes at the bottom of the page. Glue them in order in the numbered boxes on the worksheet.

✂ -

Name_____

Draw a face on the pumpkin to turn it into a jack-o'-lantern.

What's a Nut?

Objectives

Learn about nuts and solve problems.

Materials Needed

- ❑ nuts in the shell
- ❑ large bowl
- ❑ nut cracking tools
- ❑ towel
- ❑ small bowls

Setting Up the Station

- Collect a variety of nuts in their shells, such as walnuts, almonds, pecans, and filberts.
- Put the nuts in a large bowl.
- Select several nut cracking tools such as a handheld metal nutcracker, a hammer, and a rock.
- Set out the bowl of nuts, the nut cracking tools, a towel, and two small bowls.

Introducing the Project

Show your children one of each kind of nut. Help them name each one. Have them examine the nuts carefully. How are they the same? How are they different? What is inside the shell? How can they find out? Tell them they will be exploring the answers to these questions as you demonstrate the following project steps.

The Project

You may wish to have an adult supervise this project.

1. Select one of each kind of nut.

2. Look at the nuts and think of two ways they are the same (brown color, hard shell, makes a noise when shaken, etc.).

3. Select a nut to crack open.

4. Choose a nut cracking tool. If using the hammer or rock, wrap the nut in the towel before pounding to protect the table and to keep the shell pieces from flying.

5. Use your selected tool to crack open the nut. Was it easy or difficult to break the shell? What was inside?

6. Try opening up other nuts using the other tools.

7. Put the shells in one bowl and the nut meats in the other bowl.

Follow-Up

Talk about the different ways your children found to crack open the nuts. Which way was used the most? Which way worked best? Can they think of any other ways to do the job? Let the children sample the nuts they cracked. Copy the worksheets on pages 17-19 for the children to complete in class or at home.

Name_____

For each row, circle the nut that matches the nut
in the box.

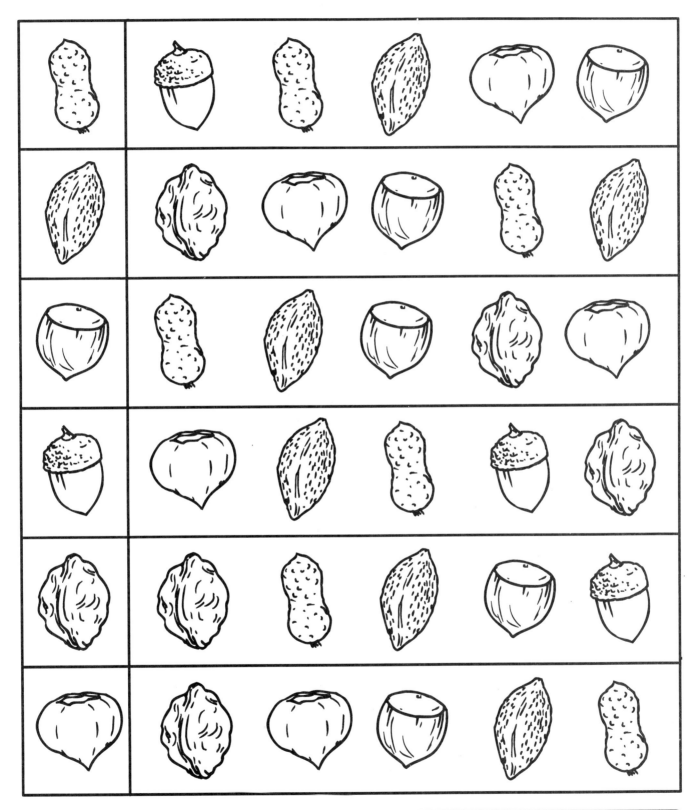

Name_____

Count the nuts in each box. Write the number on the line.

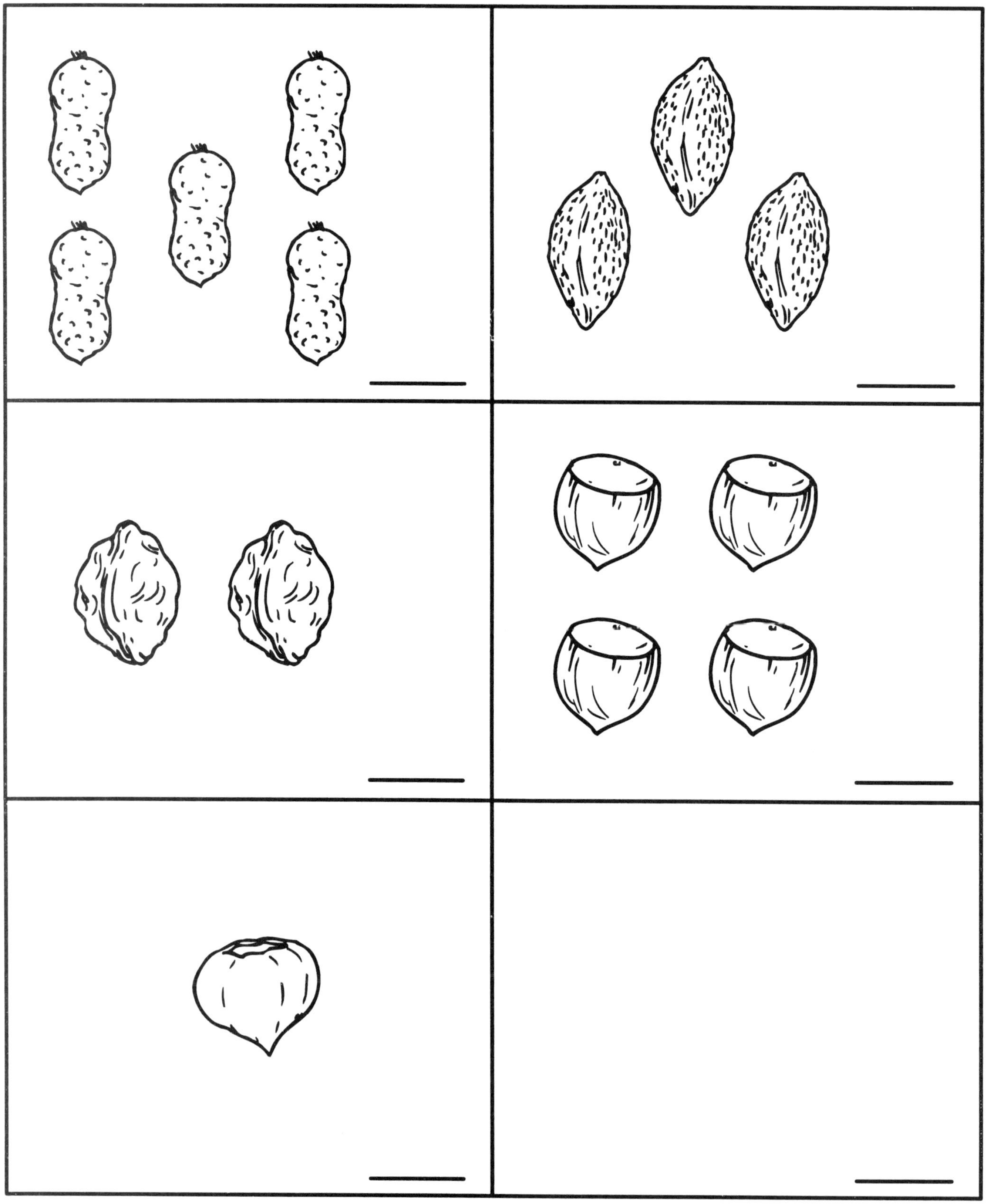

_____   _____

_____   _____

_____   _____

Name_____

The squirrel is getting ready for winter. Help it find the hidden nuts in this picture. Color the nuts brown.

Evergreen Touch

Objectives

Learn about evergreen trees, explore the sense of touch, and foster creativity.

Materials Needed

❑ evergreen sprigs
❑ tempera paint
❑ bowls
❑ apron
❑ construction paper
❑ pencil
❑ tape

Setting Up the Station

• Collect sprigs from a variety of evergreen trees such as a fir tree, a cedar tree, and a spruce tree. Be sure you have at least one for each of your children.

• Pour several colors of tempera paint into bowls.

• Set out the evergreen branches, the bowls of paint, an apron, large sheets of construction paper, a pencil, and tape.

Introducing the Project

Show your children the sprigs from the evergreen trees. Ask them if they can tell you why these trees are called evergreens (because the trees are always green, even in the winter). Have them compare the different sprigs. How are they the same? How are they different? Tell the children they will be using these evergreen sprigs in the station today, then explain the following project steps.

The Project

1. Put on the apron.

2. Look at several different evergreen sprigs. Feel each one. Which one is the softest? Which one is the most prickly?

3. Select an evergreen sprig and a sheet of construction paper.

4. Write your name on the back of the construction paper.

5. Dip the evergreen sprig into the paint. Use it as a paintbrush to draw a picture or design on the paper.

6. When you are finished, tape the sprig you used to your paper and set the paper in the designated area to dry.

Follow-Up

Hang the pictures on a wall or a bulletin board. Have your children notice what kinds of sprigs were used. Did different sprigs paint differently? Copy the worksheets on pages 21-22 for the children to complete in class or at home. If you wish, copy the Evergreen Book pattern on page 23. Have the children cut out the pages and staple them together. Let them color the evergreen tree green in each picture. Talk about how the evergreen tree stays green all year long.

Name_____

Draw a line connecting the matching evergreen branches.

Fir

Cedar

Spruce

Juniper

Name_____

Circle the objects that would feel prickly.

Fall

Winter

Spring

Summer

Snow Exploration

Objectives

Learn about snow and cold.

Materials Needed

❑ towels
❑ mittens
❑ clothesline
❑ clothespins
❑ dishpan or small cooler
❑ snow

Setting Up the Station

- Cover a table with towels.
- Collect several pairs of children's mittens and set them out.
- String a clothesline near the station and clip on several clothespins.
- Just before beginning the station, fill a dishpan or a small plastic foam cooler with snow. (If you do not have snow, use ice cubes instead.)

Introducing the Project

Talk about snow with your children. Is snow hot or cold? What kind of clothes do you wear when it snows? Let your children explore snow after you explain the following project steps. (Hint: You will probably need to replace the snow or ice cubes throughout the day.)

The Project

1. Examine the snow with your hands. What does it feel like? What happens to the cold snow when you hold it with your warm hands? What happens to your hands? Put your hands on your cheeks. Are your hands warm or cold now?

2. Put on a pair of the mittens. How do your hands feel now?

3. Wearing the mittens, play with the snow some more. Are your hands getting cold or staying warm? What is happening to the snow?

4. When you are finished, hang your mittens on the clothesline to dry.

Follow-Up

Talk with your children about what the snow was like. How did it feel? What could they do with it? What happened to the snow when it was in their warm hands and in the warm room? Copy the worksheets on pages 25-27 for the children to complete in class or at home.

Name_____

Circle the clothes you wear in the snow.

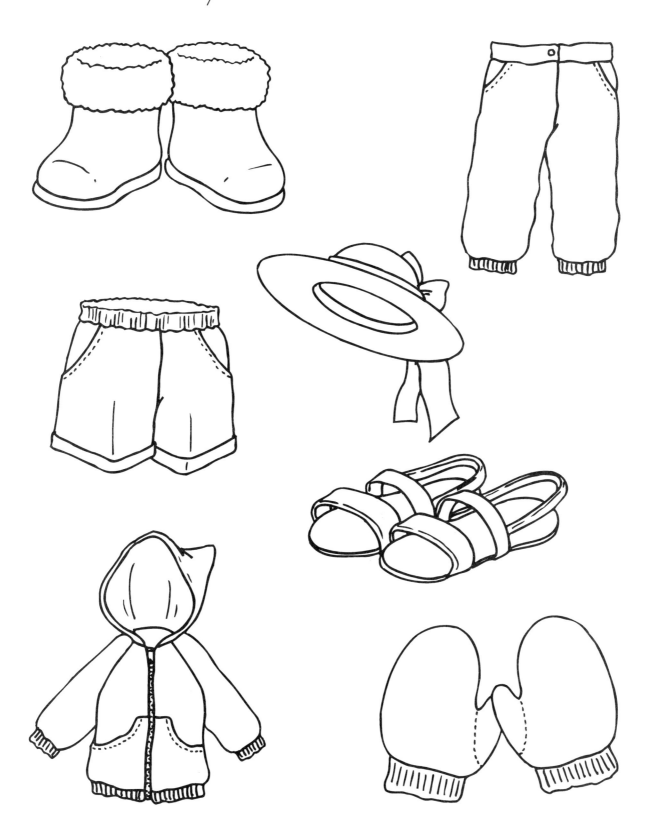

Name_____

Connect the dots.

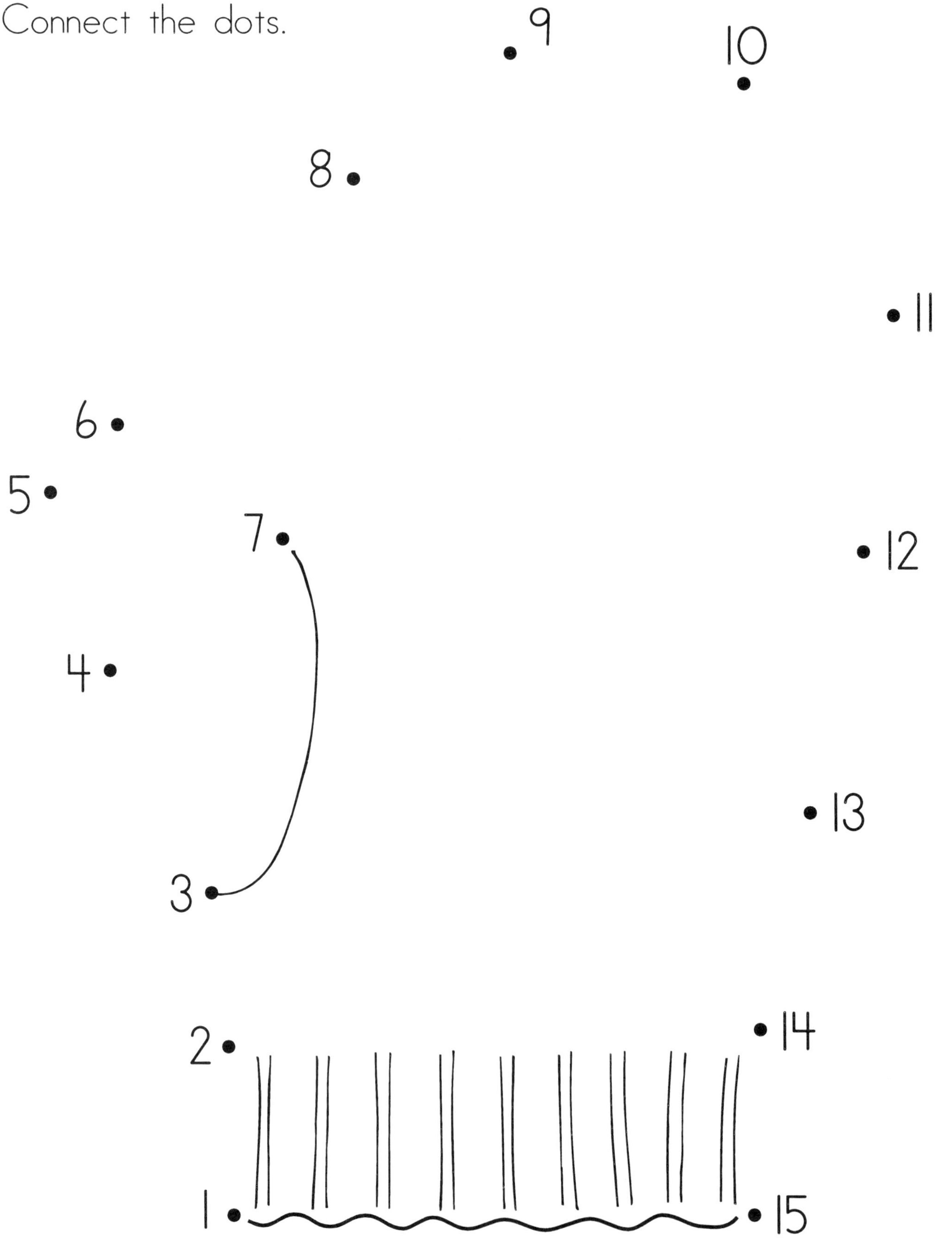

9

10

8

11

6

5

7

12

4

3

13

2   14

1   15

Name_____

Draw a face and other details to complete the snow friend.

Sand Safari

Objectives

Explore sand and use a magnifying glass.

Materials Needed

- ❑ sand
- ❑ dishpan
- ❑ rocks
- ❑ shells
- ❑ paper plates
- ❑ magnifying glass

Setting Up the Station

- Put some sand in a dishpan.
- Collect several rocks and shells. Try to find rocks and shells with the same colors as the grains of sand.
- Set out the sand, the rocks and shells, paper plates, and a magnifying glass.

Introducing the Station

Discuss sand with your children. Ask them to name the different places where they see sand. How is sand made? Tell them that powerful waves of water grind rocks and shells into tiny pieces. Then explain the following project steps to the children.

The Project

1. Sprinkle some sand on a paper plate.

2. Spread out the sand so you can see some of the individual grains.

3. Use the magnifying glass to look at the grains of sand. How many different colors do you see?

4. Compare the grains of sand to the shells and rocks. Which grains of sand do you think are from shells? Which ones are from rocks? How are the grains of sand the same as the rocks and shells (color, texture, etc.)? How are they different (size, shape, etc.)?

5. When you are finished with your comparisons, carefully pour the sand back into the dishpan.

Follow-Up

Let your children try making their own sand. Put a few small rocks and shells in a plastic jar. Fill the jar about three-fourths full of water. Tightly secure the lid on the jar. Let the children take turns shaking the jar to create "waves." After several minutes of shaking, have the children check the jar for grains of sand—there should be at least a few. Copy the worksheets on pages 29-31 for the children to complete in class or at home.

Name_____

Count the grains of sand under each magnifying glass. Write the number on the line.

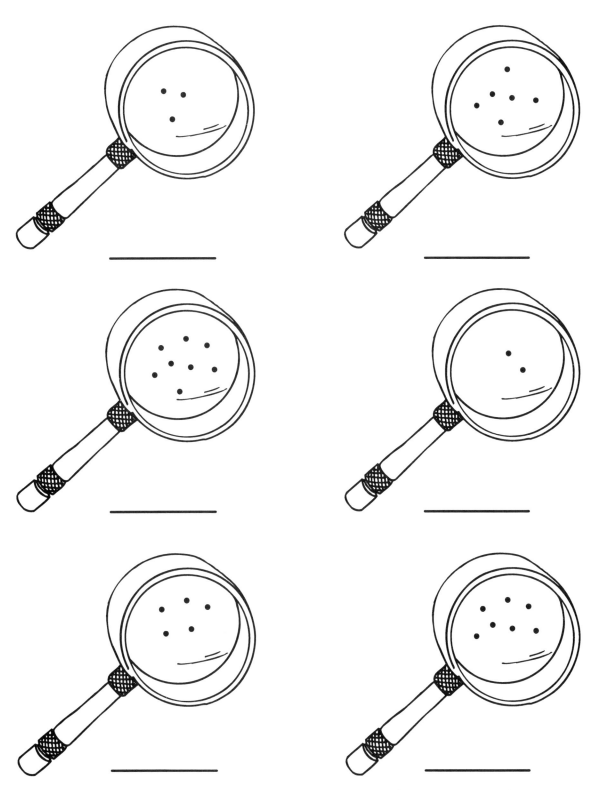

Name_____

Find the path through the ocean waves to
reach the sandy beach.

Name_____

Draw a sand castle you would like to build.

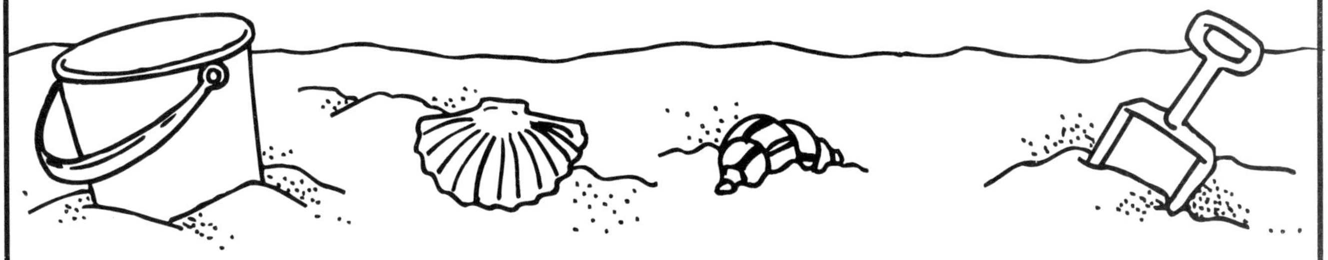

Planter

Objectives

Make a planter and learn about what plants need to grow.

Materials Needed

❑ clear-plastic cups
❑ small plants
❑ bowl
❑ water
❑ potting soil
❑ bucket
❑ spoon
❑ eyedropper
❑ masking tape
❑ pencil

Setting Up the Station

- Collect a clear-plastic cup for each of your children.
- Grow or purchase a small plant for each child. (Marigolds work well.)
- Fill a bowl with water.
- Pour potting soil into a bucket and add a spoon.
- Set out the cups, the plants, the bowl of water, the potting soil and spoon, an eyedropper, masking tape, and a pencil.

Introducing the Project

Talk about plants with your children. What do plants need to grow? (Food from the soil, water, and sunlight.) Explain to the children that they will be planting plants to take home and care for; then demonstrate the following steps.

The Project

1. Select one of the cups.

2. Tear off a piece of masking tape and write your name on it. Put the tape on the bottom of your cup.

3. Use the spoon to fill your cup most of the way with some soil.

4. Carefully make a small hole in the soil, and gently place the roots of one of the plants in it. Gently fill the hole with dirt to surround the plant.

5. Use the eyedropper to sprinkle the soil and plant with water.

6. Take the plant home and keep it in a sunny window.

Follow-Up

Ask permission to plant and care for a section of your school's grounds, or purchase a window box for your classroom. Let the children plan which plants they would like to grow there. Have them plant and take care of those plants. Copy the worksheets on pages 33-35 for the children to complete in class or at home.

Name_____

Draw a line from the plant to each of the things it needs to grow.

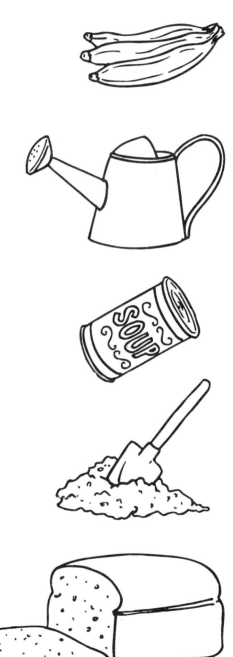

Name_____

Circle the things that grow in a garden.

Name_____

Draw your own garden.

Flower Power

Objectives

Discover the parts of a flower and use a magnifying glass.

Materials Needed

❑ flowers
❑ magnifying glass
❑ worksheet
❑ crayons

Setting Up the Station

• Collect at least one fresh flower for each of your children. (Daisies work well for this activity.)
• Copy the Flower Parts worksheet on page 37.
• Set out the flowers, a magnifying glass, the copies of the worksheet, and crayons.

Introducing the Project

Show your children one of the flowers and a copy of the Flower Parts worksheet. Point out the parts of the flower on the worksheet and then on the flower. Explain that in the station they will be looking at all of the flower parts with a magnifying glass; then demonstrate the following steps to your children.

The Project

1. Select one of the flowers.
2. Look at the flower with and without the magnifying glass. What colors do you see?
3. Carefully pull off one of the petals. Look at it with the magnifying glass. If you wish, count the petals.
4. Use the magnifying glass to look at the other parts of the flower.
5. Color the Flower Parts worksheet to match your flower.

Follow-Up

Bring in a vase of flowers for your children to enjoy. Challenge them to find the petals, stem, and leaves on each different kind. Copy the worksheets on pages 38-39 for the children to work on in class or at home.

Name_____

Color the flower. Name the parts.

Name_____

For each flower, identify the number in the center and draw on that many petals.

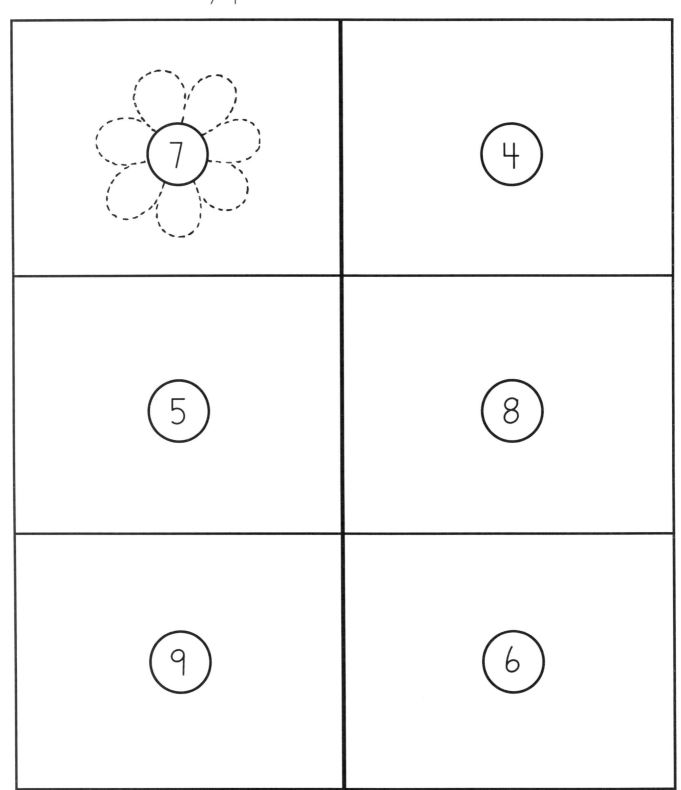

Name_____

Draw lines to connect the flowers that match.

Investigating Water and Air

What Floats?

Objectives

Discover which objects float and which objects sink.

Materials Needed

❑ small objects
❑ towel
❑ dishpan
❑ water
❑ worksheet
❑ pencil

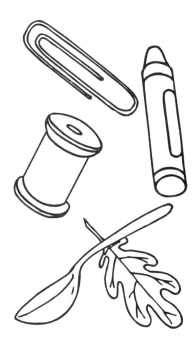

Setting Up the Station

- Collect the following small objects: a paper clip, a small piece of paper, a pebble, a wooden or plastic spool, a metal spoon, a crayon, a coin, and a leaf.
- Place the objects on a towel.
- Find a dishpan and fill it halfway with water.
- Copy the Sink or Float worksheet on page 43.
- Set out the towel with the small objects, the dishpan of water, the copies of the worksheet, and a pencil.

Introducing the Project

Ask your children to name things they can think of that float in the water and other things that sink. Tell them that they will be experimenting with objects to find out which ones sink and which ones float. Explain the following steps to your children.

The Project

1. Take a copy of the worksheet and write your name on it.
2. Find the first object shown on the worksheet.
3. Put that object in the water. Observe as it sinks or floats.
4. If it floats, put an *X* by the object's name under the Floats column. If it sinks, put an *X* by the name under the Sinks column.
5. Take the object out of the water and place it on the towel to dry for the next person.
6. Repeat with the remaining objects.

Follow-Up

Fill a big clear jar with water. Let your children test various (waterproof) objects from the classroom to see which ones float and which ones sink. Copy the worksheets on pages 44-45 for the children to work on in class or at home.

Name_____

For each item, put an X in the correct column.

Object		
paper clip 		
paper 		
rock 		
spool 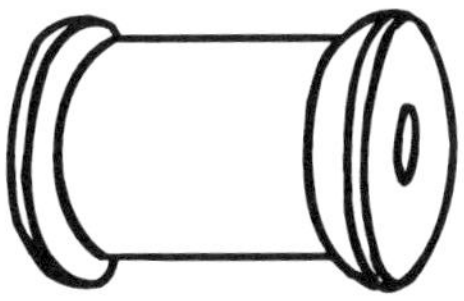		
spoon 		
crayon		
coin 		
leaf 		

Name_____

Circle the objects that float.

Name_____

On the top of the water, draw something that floats.
At the bottom of the jar, draw something that sinks.

Ball or Boat?

Objectives

Discover which shapes float best.

Materials Needed

❑ modeling clay
❑ container
❑ dishpan
❑ water
❑ worksheet
❑ pencil
❑ towel

Setting Up the Station

• Put some modeling clay in a container.
• Fill a dishpan about halfway with water.
• Copy the Floating Shapes worksheet on page 47.
• Set out the container of clay, the dishpan of water, the copies of the worksheet, a pencil, and a towel.

Introducing the Project

Talk about things that float. Ask your children to think about the shapes that those things have in common. Tell them they will be experimenting with different shapes to find out which ones float best. Explain the following project steps to the children.

The Project

1. Take a copy of the worksheet and write your name on it.

2. Look at the first shape on the worksheet. Take a handful of clay and form it into that shape.

3. Carefully put the shape into the water in the dishpan, and observe. Does the shape sink or float? If it floats, draw a circle around the picture of the shape on the worksheet. If it sinks, cross it out.

4. Using the same modeling clay, repeat with the other shapes. (You may need to pat the clay dry with the towel between making each shape.)

5. Put the clay back in the container and dry your hands on the towel.

Follow-Up

Ask the children to tell you about their floating experiments. Which shapes floated? Which ones sank? What do the floating shapes have in common with boats? Copy the worksheets on pages 48-49 for the children to complete in class or at home.

Name_____

Circle the shapes that float. Cross out the shapes that sink.

Name_____

Draw lines to connect the boats that match.

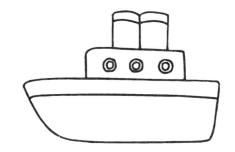

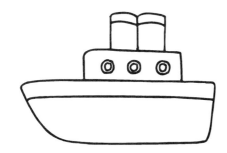

Name_____

Color the picture. ☆=red △=blue
□=yellow ○=green

Make a Boat

Objectives

Design and test-float a boat.

Materials Needed

❑ dishpan
❑ water
❑ containers
❑ straws
❑ paper
❑ scissors
❑ tape
❑ crayons
❑ modeling dough
❑ small plastic boats

Setting Up the Station

• Fill a dishpan about halfway with water.

• Collect a variety of plastic containers such as cottage cheese and margarine tubs, tops and bottoms of takeout containers, and bakery food trays. (Ask parents to save these at home and send them in.)

• Find plastic drinking straws and various colors and kinds of paper.

• Set out the plastic containers, straws, paper, scissors, tape, crayons, and a small container of modeling dough.

Introducing the Project

Show your children several small plastic boats. Float them on the water in the dishpan. Tell the children that they will be making their own boats today, then demonstrate the following steps.

The Project

1. Choose one of the plastic containers for your boat. Decorate the container with crayons, if you wish.

2. Select a sheet of paper and cut a triangular shape out of it for a sail.

3. Decorate the sail with crayon designs. Write your name on it.

4. Tape the sail to a straw.

5. Roll a small ball of modeling dough and put it in the bottom of your boat. Stick the straw with the sail attached to it into the dough. Add additional sails if you would like.

6. Try floating your boat in the tub. If it does not float well, adjust the sails and modeling dough as needed and try again.

Follow-Up

Set up a mini-"lake," such as a wading pool or a water table, or find a large puddle. Let your children float their boats in the lake and blow on the sails to make them move. Talk about real boats with your children. Why do people use boats? Who sails on a boat? Copy the worksheets on pages 51-53 for the children to work on in class or at home.

Name_____

Design your very own boat.

Name_____

Connect the dots to complete the boat.

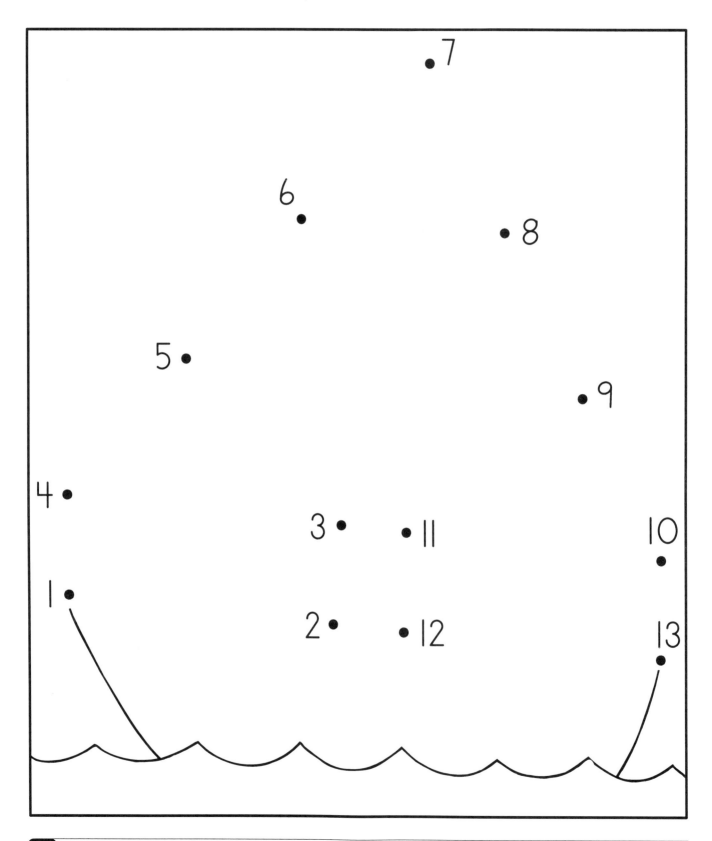

Name_____

Help the sailor find her boat.

Water Sandwich

Objectives
Observe and work carefully.

Materials Needed
❏ water
❏ pitchers
❏ food coloring
❏ vegetable oil
❏ honey
❏ worksheet
❏ sink
❏ glass or jar
❏ spoon
❏ pencil
❏ crayons

Setting Up the Station
- Fill a small pitcher with water and add several drops of food coloring (blue or green works best).
- Fill a second small pitcher with vegetable oil.
- Purchase honey in a squeezable container.
- Copy the Sandwich Colors worksheet on page 55.
- Make sure a sink is available for cleanup.
- Set out the pitchers of water and oil, the honey, a clear drinking glass or jar, a spoon, a pencil, and crayons.

Introducing the Project
While your children watch, prepare a Water Sandwich following steps 1-4 below. Explain that the water is lighter (less dense) than the honey, so it floats on top of it. The oil is even lighter (less dense) than the water, so it floats on top of it. Then go over all of the following project steps with your children. (You may want an adult helper at this station.)

The Project
1. Squeeze enough honey into the glass to completely cover the bottom of the glass.
2. Carefully pour water into the glass to cover up the honey.
3. Slowly pour on enough oil to cover up the water.
4. Examine the three layers of liquid. Which one is on the bottom? Which one is on the top?
5. Take the spoon and gently stir the liquids together. Observe as they separate into three layers again.
6. Take a copy of the worksheet. Write your name on it. Color the layers on the worksheet to match the colors of your liquid layers.
7. Empty the liquids into a sink and rinse out the glass with warm water.

Follow-Up
Ask your children to tell you what they observed with the three liquids. What happened after they were mixed together? Together, make another Water Sandwich in a jar with a lid. Securely fasten the lid and wrap it with duct tape. Let your children take turns shaking the jar and watching the layers separate.

Name_____

Color the layers to match yours.

Name_____

For each row, number the first step "1," the second step "2," and the third step "3."

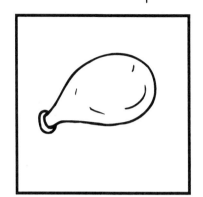
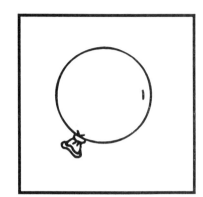

_____   _____   _____

_____   _____   _____

_____   _____   _____

Name_____

In each box, circle the object in the middle.

Dancing Raisins

Objectives

Follow directions and observe.

Materials Needed

❑ pitcher
❑ water
❑ clear-plastic cups
❑ permanent marker
❑ vinegar
❑ squeeze bottle
❑ baking soda
❑ bowls
❑ raisins
❑ worksheet
❑ measuring spoons
❑ sink

Setting Up the Station

• Fill a small pitcher with water.

• Collect a clear-plastic cup for each of your children. Use a permanent marker to draw a line at the halfway point on each cup.

• Put vinegar into a plastic squeeze bottle.

• Scoop some baking soda into one bowl and some raisins into another bowl.

• Copy the Dancing Raisins worksheet on page 59 and hang it up in the station.

• Set out the water pitcher, the cups, the vinegar bottle, the bowls of baking soda and raisins, and measuring spoons.

Introducing the Project

Tell the children that they will have the opportunity to make raisins dance with this station activity. Show them the copy of the Dancing Raisins worksheet as you explain the following steps. (You may wish to have an adult supervise this activity.)

The Project

1. Choose a cup and fill it with water up to the line.

2. Measure 1 tablespoon of vinegar into the water.

3. Put in five raisins.

4. Add 1 teaspoon of baking soda.

5. Watch the raisins dance.

6. Pour the water into the sink. Throw away the raisins and the cup.

Follow-Up

Ask your children to tell you what happened at each step of their investigation. What happened when they added the vinegar to the water? The raisins? The baking soda? Did all of the raisins dance? What was in all those bubbles? (Air.) Copy the worksheets on pages 60-61 for the children to work on in class or at home.

Dancing Raisins

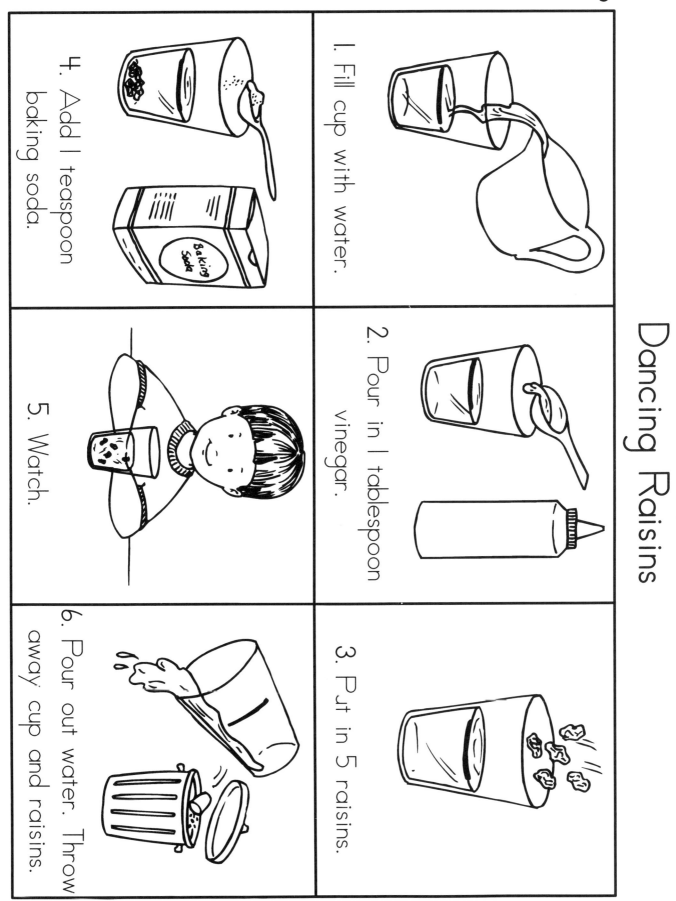

1. Fill cup with water.

2. Pour in 1 tablespoon vinegar.

3. Put in 5 raisins.

4. Add 1 teaspoon baking soda.

5. Watch.

6. Pour out water. Throw away cup and raisins.

Name_____

Follow the path of each dancing raisin.

Name_____

Help the raisin dance to the top of the glass.

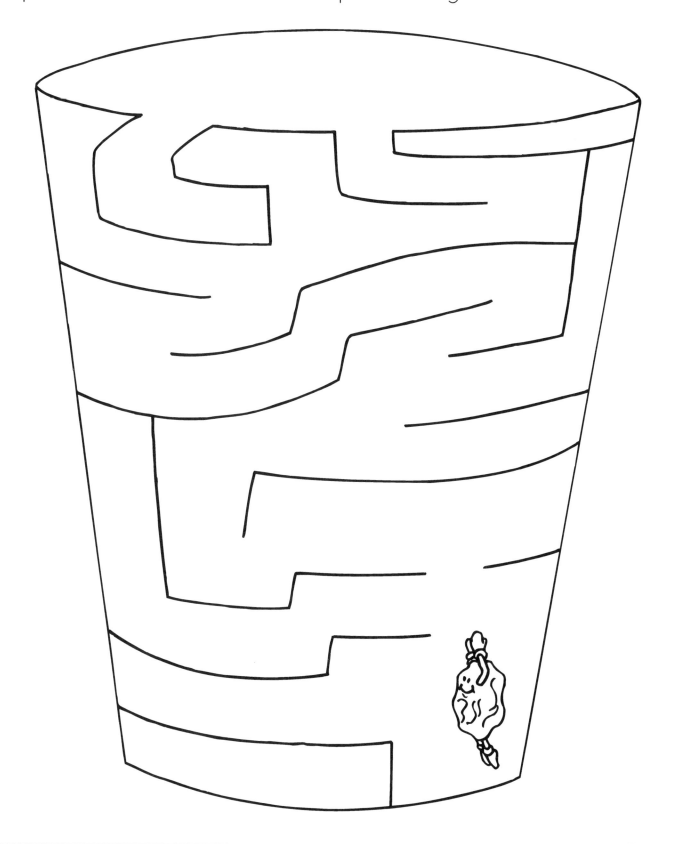

Magical Air

Objectives

Learn that air takes up space.

Materials Needed

❑ large clear bowl
❑ water
❑ scissors
❑ sponge
❑ clear-plastic cup
❑ paper napkins

Setting Up the Station

• Fill a large clear bowl with water and set it on the table in the station.
• Cut a sponge into four to six small pieces.
• Set out the sponge pieces, a clear-plastic cup, and some paper napkins.

Introducing the Project

Explain to your children that air is all around them and that even though they can't feel or see it, it takes up space. To demonstrate, crumple one of the paper napkins and put it in the bottom of the clear-plastic cup. Turn the cup upside down and hold it steady while you push the cup into the bowl of water. Carefully lift the cup out of the water and show your children the dry paper napkin. Why did it stay dry? (Because the air in the cup took up the space between the napkin and the water.) Tell your children they will be experimenting with air and water today; then explain the following project steps to them.

The Project

1. Crumple up a paper napkin and put it in the clear-plastic cup.
2. Turn the cup upside down and hold it steady as you push the cup into the bowl of water. (If you tilt the cup, water will get in.)
3. Take the cup out and feel your napkin. Is it dry or wet?
4. Now float one of the sponge pieces on the water. Turn the plastic cup upside down over the sponge piece. Push down on the cup. What is happening to the sponge? What is pushing the sponge down? (Air.)
5. Try floating more than one sponge piece. How many pieces can you push down at one time?

Follow-Up

Encourage your children to think of other examples of air taking up space, such as in a balloon, an inflatable ball, an air mattress, a tire, and bubbles. Copy the worksheets on pages 63-65 for the children to work on in class or at home.

Name_____

For each pair of objects, circle the one that has air in it.

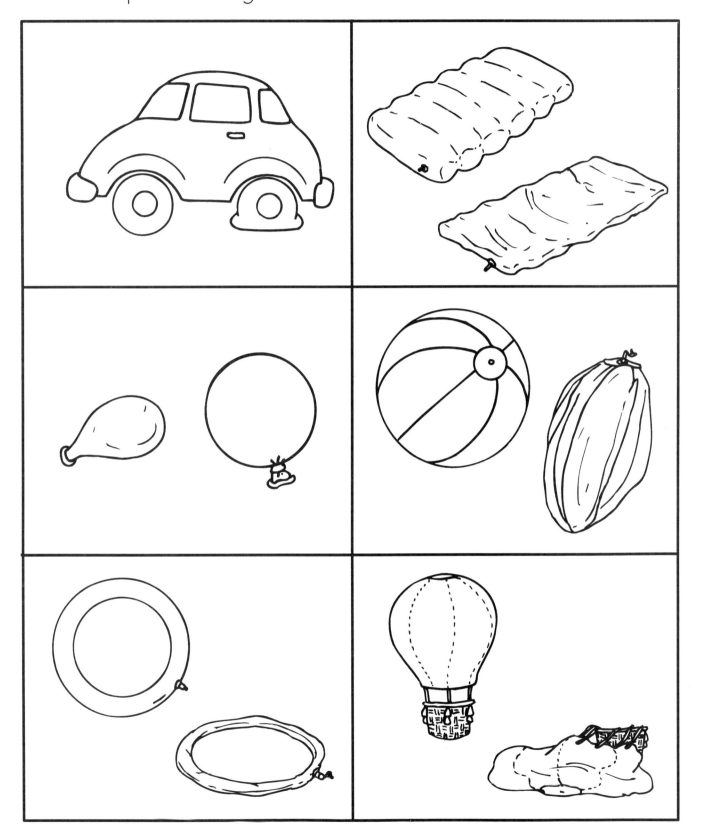

Name_____

For each group, count the balloons and write
the number on the line.

Name

Color the hot air balloon.

Air Lab

Objectives

Experiment with and learn about air.

Materials Needed

❑ straws
❑ household objects
❑ basket

Setting Up the Station

• Collect a plastic drinking straw for each of your children.
• Find a variety of household objects, some lightweight (a cotton ball, a feather, a piece of paper, etc.) and some heavyweight (a rock, a block, a measuring cup, etc.). Put the objects in a basket.
• Set out the straws and the basket of objects.

Introducing the Project

Ask your children to tell you about times when they knew air was moving (wind, air from a fan, blowing out a candle, etc.). How did they know it was moving? Tell them they will be experimenting with air to find out things it can move and things it cannot move. Then explain the following project steps to them.

The Project

1. Select one of the straws. Practice blowing out through the straw.
2. Choose one of the items from the basket and place it on the table.
3. Predict whether or not you will be able to move the object just by blowing on it through the straw.
4. Try moving the object by blowing on it. Did it move?
5. Repeat with the other objects.

Follow-Up

Show your children the objects they tried to move with their air. Which ones could they move? Which ones could they not move? What do the objects that moved have in common? How were the objects that did not move alike? Ask them to tell you what kinds of things they see moving when the wind blows. Copy the worksheets on pages 67-69 for the children to work on in class or at home.

Name_____

Count the number of cotton balls each child is moving with air. Draw a line to that number.

4

3

6

7

2

Name_____

The wind has blown away the people's hats.
Can you find them? Color the hats.

Name_____

Connect the dots to find out what the wind is moving now.

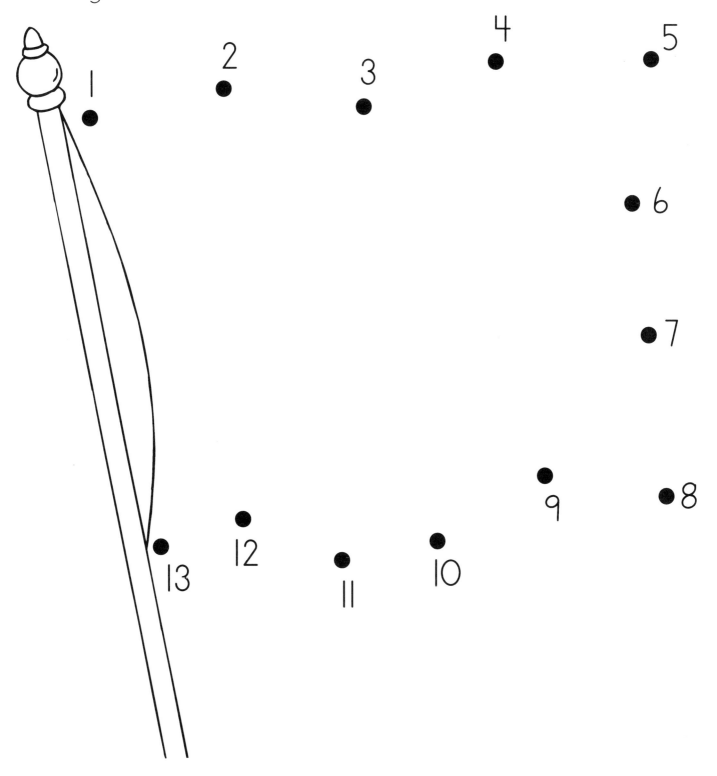

Investigating the Body and the Senses

Hear Your Heart

Objectives

Listen to your heartbeat and learn about keeping your heart healthy.

Materials Needed

❑ stethoscope

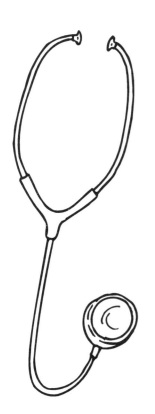

Setting Up the Station

• Find a good-quality stethoscope. (Check a local medical supply store for one.)
• Set out the stethoscope.

Introducing the Station

Ask your children to tell you what they know about their heart. (It pumps blood through the body; you can hear it beating sometimes; it's about the size of their fist; etc.) Have them show you where their heart is. Explain that they will be able to hear their heart beating when they do the station project. Show them how to use a stethoscope. Then explain and demonstrate the following steps to them. (You may wish to have an adult at the station to assist the children.)

The Project

1. Sit down at the table. Use the stethoscope to listen carefully to your heart. Is your heart beating quickly or slowly?
2. Jog in place while you slowly count to 20.
3. Sit down and use the stethoscope to listen to your heart again. How is it beating this time?
4. Jump up and down 20 times.
5. Sit down and listen to your heart again. Is it beating faster or slower than last time?

Follow-Up

Let your children tell you about their heartbeats. When did their heart beat the fastest? When did it beat the slowest? Explain that the heart pumps their blood through their body. When they exercise, their body needs more blood, so the heart beats faster. This exercise makes their heart stronger. Talk about ways the children can take care of their hearts by exercising, getting lots of rest, eating healthy foods, and so on. If you wish, copy the worksheets on pages 73–75 for the children to work on in class or at home.

Name _____

Color the heart.

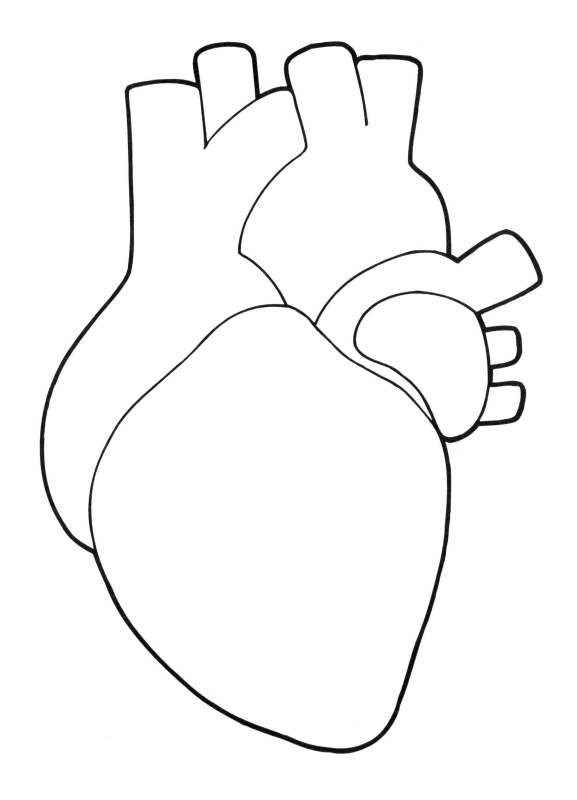

Name_____

Draw lines showing how blood is pumped out from the heart to other parts of the body and back.

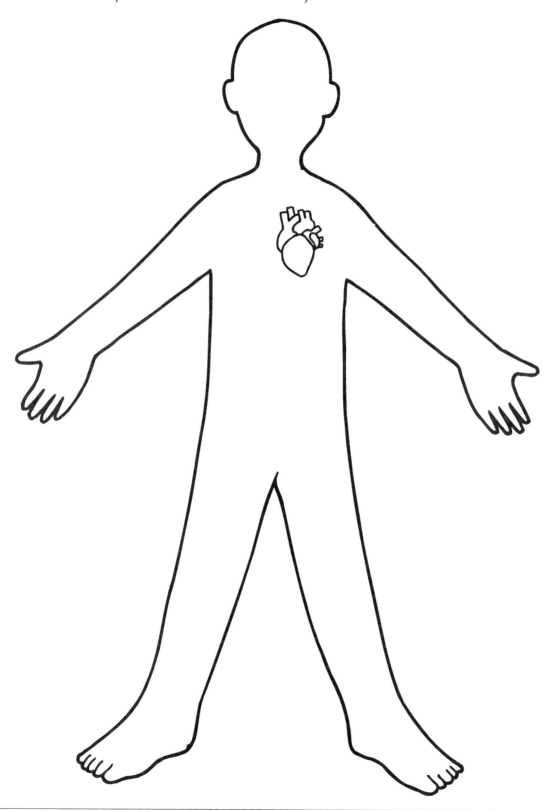

Name_____

Circle the things you do to keep your heart healthy.

X-Ray Fun

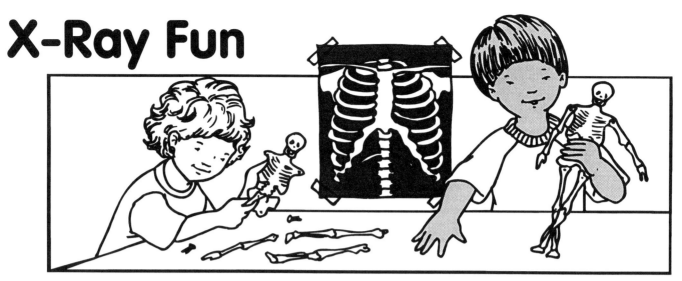

Objectives

Learn about the skeleton.

Materials Needed

❑ x-ray picture

❑ skeleton or picture of skeleton

❑ worksheets

❑ scissors

❑ brass paper fasteners

❑ pencil

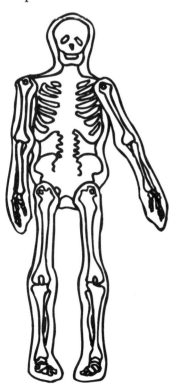

Setting Up the Station

• Find an x-ray. Your doctor or dentist may have one you can have or borrow.

• Try to borrow a skeleton to set up in your class. A high school science teacher may have one you can use for a while. Or find a picture of a skeleton at the library.

• Copy the Skeleton Pattern worksheets on pages 77-78.

• Set out the x-ray, the skeleton or skeleton picture, the copies of the worksheets, scissors, brass paper fasteners, and a pencil.

Introducing the Station

Show your children the skeleton or skeleton picture. Ask them what it is. Tell them they have bones like these in their body. Have them feel their wrist bones or knee bones. Can they find any other bones in their body? Talk about how the bones in their bodies hold them up and protect their brain, heart, lungs, and other organs. Then explain the following project steps to the children.

The Project

1. Look at the x-ray by holding it up to the light. Where are the bones? Try to find those bones on the skeleton or the picture of the skeleton.

2. Take a copy of each of the worksheets. Cut on the dotted lines to cut out the skeleton pieces.

3. Put the skeleton together by matching up the dots and attaching the pieces together with brass paper fasteners.

4. Write your name on the back of your skeleton.

Follow-Up

Have your children show you their skeletons. Hang the skeletons on a wall or a bulletin board. Talk about the different bones they see. Do all animals have bones? If you wish, copy the worksheet on page 79 for the children to finish in class or at home.

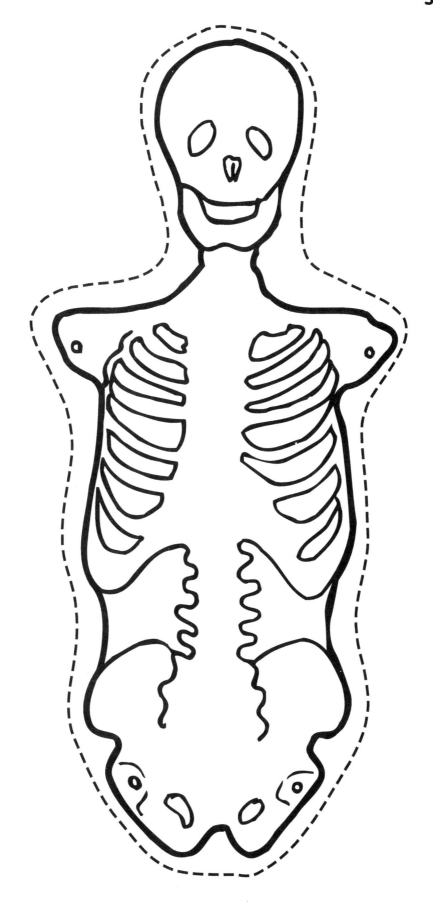

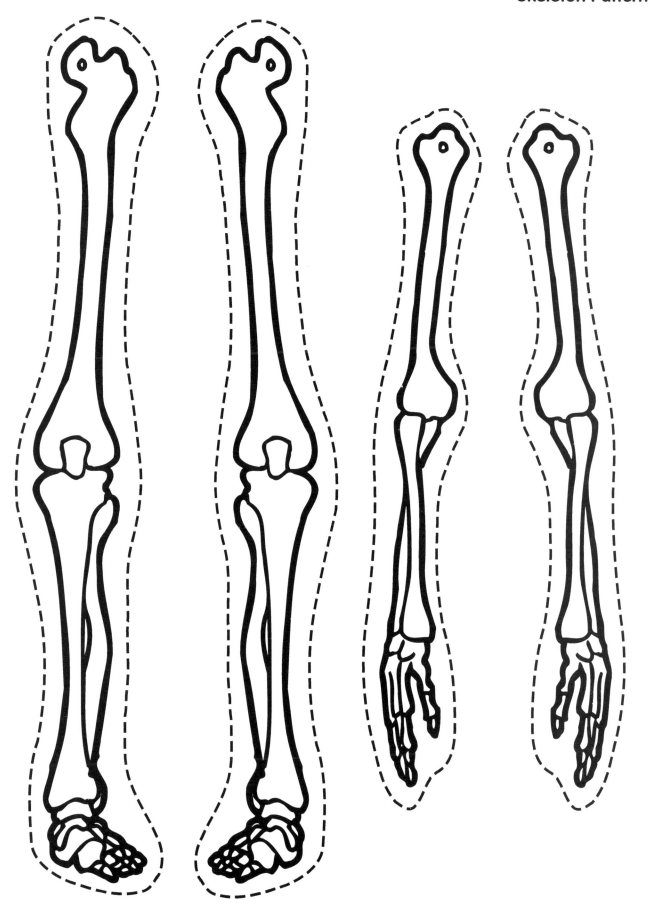

Name_____

Draw a line from each animal to its skeleton.

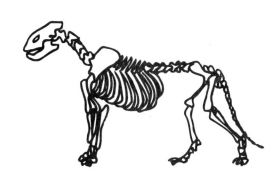

My Body

Objectives

Learn about the unique features of your body.

Materials Needed

- ❑ scale
- ❑ measuring tape or growth chart
- ❑ mirror
- ❑ worksheets
- ❑ pencil
- ❑ crayons
- ❑ stapler

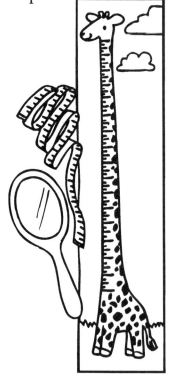

Setting Up the Station

- Find a scale and place it in the station.
- Post a measuring tape or growth chart on a wall by the station.
- Have a hand mirror or other kind of mirror available near the station.
- Copy the worksheets on pages 81-83.
- Set out the copies of the worksheets, a pencil, crayons (regular and multicultural crayons work well for this project), and a stapler.

Introducing the Project

Discuss with your children how each of them has a body that is unique. Encourage them to think about the ways that their bodies are special. Each body has its own size; shape; and colors of hair, eyes, and skin. Tell the children they will be exploring some of the unique characteristics of their bodies in the station project. Then explain the following project steps to them. (You may wish to have an adult helper at this station.)

The Project

1. Take a copy of the All About Me worksheet. Stand on the scale to find out how many pounds you weigh and write that number on the first line. Measure yourself on the measuring tape to find out how many inches tall you are and write that number on the second line. Look in the mirror as you draw a picture of yourself at the bottom of the page. Find the crayon colors that match your colors.

2. Pick up a copy of the This Is My Hand worksheet. Place one hand on the worksheet and trace around it. Add details to your hand tracing, if you wish.

3. Take a copy of the This Is My Foot worksheet. Place the worksheet on the floor and put one foot on it. Trace around your foot. Add a shoe or other details as you want.

4. Write your name on your worksheets and staple them together to make a book about yourself.

Follow-Up

Divide the children into pairs. Let the pairs of children share their books with each other. Reinforce the idea that every person's body is unique and special.

Name_____

Weigh and measure yourself.
Fill in the blanks.

I weigh _____ pounds.

I am _____ inches tall.

Draw a picture of yourself.

Name_____

Trace around your hand.

Name_____

Trace around your foot.

Look and See

Objectives

Observe and use a magnifying glass.

Materials Needed

❑ magnifying glass
❑ small objects
❑ black construction paper

Setting Up the Station

• Find a good, sturdy magnifying glass for your children to use.
• Collect a variety of small objects to examine, such as a leaf, a rock, a photograph, a picture from a magazine, a toy, and a piece of fabric.
• Set out the magnifying glass, the objects, and a sheet of black construction paper.

Introducing the Project

Talk with your children about how they use their eyes to see the world around them. Ask them to tell you some of the things they see now. Show them the magnifying glass. Tell them that this special glass allows them to see even more things because when they look through it, everything looks bigger. Then explain the following project steps.

The Project

1. Select one of the objects and place it on the black construction paper.

2. Look at the object with and without the magnifying glass. What can you see with the magnifying glass that you couldn't see without it?

3. Repeat with the other objects.

Follow-Up

Collect a small plastic magnifying glass for each of your children. Let them take their magnifying glasses on a nature hike. What new things can they see with their magnifying glasses? Copy the worksheets on pages 85-87 for the children to complete in class or at home.

Name_____

Look at the part of the object shown in each magnifying glass. Draw a line to the matching whole object.

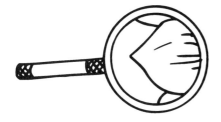

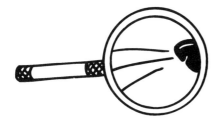 

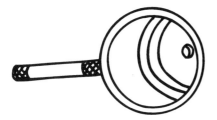 

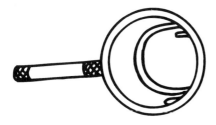

Name_____

Find these objects in the picture.

Name_____

The detective is searching for clues. Help him find the next clue.

Touch This

Objectives

Explore through the sense of touch and identify objects by touch.

Materials Needed

❑ shoeboxes
❑ sharp knife
❑ permanent marker
❑ household objects
❑ tape
❑ worksheet
❑ pencil

Setting Up the Station

- Collect six shoeboxes.
- Use a sharp knife to cut a small hole (large enough for a child's hand to fit through) in one side of each shoebox. Number the boxes from 1 to 6 with a permanent marker.
- Find a spoon, a crayon, a sock, a toy car, a block, and a small rubber ball. Put one object in each box.
- Fasten the lids to the boxes with tape to complete the "feeling boxes."
- Copy the What Is It? worksheet on page 89.
- Set out the feeling boxes, the copies of the worksheet, and a pencil.

Introducing the Project

Ask your children to touch their own shirts. How do they feel? Have them touch their shoes. Do their shoes feel the same as their shirts? Encourage them to tell you about all the different things they can feel through their sense of touch. Provide them with sensory words, such as *soft, smooth, hard, rough,* and *prickly,* as needed. Then explain the following project steps to the children.

The Project

1. Take a copy of the worksheet and write your name on it.
2. Find feeling box number 1.
3. Put your hand through the hole on the side of the box so you can feel the object.
4. Think of one way to describe how the object feels, then guess what it is.
5. Find box number 1 on the worksheet. Draw a line from the box to the object that you think is inside of it.
6. Continue with the remaining boxes.

Follow-Up

While your children watch, open up the feeling boxes. How well did they guess the objects inside? Could they figure out what most of the objects were? Copy the worksheets on pages 90-91 for the children to work on in class or at home.

Name_____

Draw a line from each box to the object
that is inside of it.

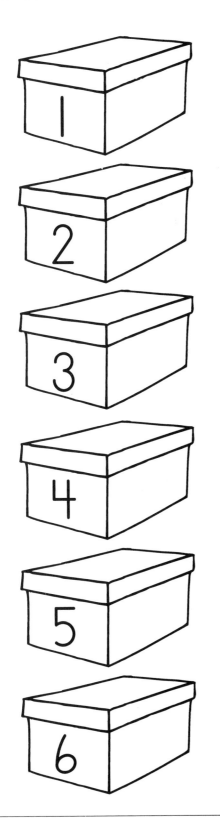

Name‗‗‗‗‗‗‗‗‗‗‗‗‗‗‗‗‗‗‗‗‗‗‗‗‗‗‗

Draw a line to connect the items that
feel the same.

Name_____

Connect the dots to discover what
the girl likes to touch.

Musical Sounds

Objectives

Listen carefully, learn about high and low pitches, and match sounds.

Materials Needed

❑ glass jars
❑ ruler
❑ permanent marker
❑ water
❑ worksheet
❑ metal spoon

Setting Up the Station

• Collect four identical glass jars. Leave one jar plain. Use a permanent marker to draw a line 1 inch from the bottom on one jar. Draw a line 1 inch from the top on another jar. Draw a line in the middle for the last jar.

• Fill three of the jars with water up to the lines. (The plain jar remains empty.)

• Copy the Play It worksheet on page 93.

• Arrange the jars from empty to full on the table. Set out the copies of the worksheet and a metal spoon.

Introducing the Project

Talk with your children about their sense of hearing. What kinds of sounds do they hear? Sing a simple song with your children. Ask them to listen carefully for the different sounds they make as they sing. Have them sing the song in very low voices, then in very high voices. Can they hear the difference between the high notes and the low notes? Sing several notes for your children and ask them to tell you if they are high notes or low notes. Then explain the following project steps to the children.

The Project

1. Use the spoon to gently tap the rim of each jar.

2. Listen carefully to the notes. Which jar makes the highest note? Which jar makes the lowest?

3. Take a copy of the worksheet. See how the four jars on the worksheet match yours.

4. Play a song by tapping each jar in the order you see on the worksheet.

5. Experiment with making up your own song from the notes.

Follow-Up

Set up a real xylophone. Let your children take turns playing it and finding the high and low notes. Copy the worksheets on pages 94-95 for the children to work on in class or at home.

Name_____

Name_____

In each box, circle the jar that does
not make the same sound as the others.

Name_____

For each box, count the number of keys
the xylophone has. Circle that number.

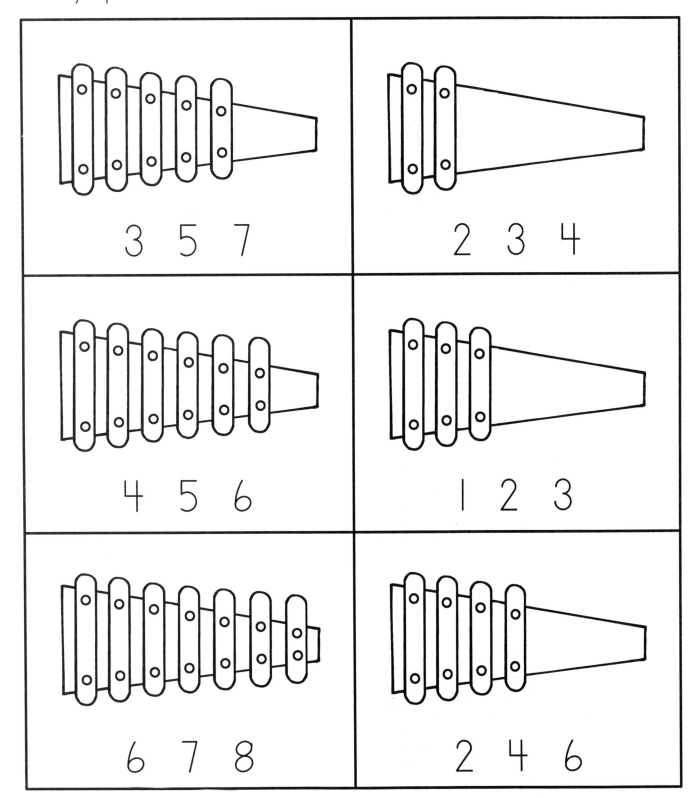

3 5 7

2 3 4

4 5 6

1 2 3

6 7 8

2 4 6

Smelling Jars

Objectives

Experiment with the sense of smell.

Materials Needed

❑ yogurt containers
❑ nail
❑ scented materials
❑ cotton balls

Setting Up the Station

- Collect eight to ten yogurt containers with lids. Use a small nail to poke four holes in each lid.
- Collect a variety of scented materials such as vanilla extract, ground cloves, ground cinnamon, perfume, and lemon juice.
- Put two cotton balls in each yogurt container.
- Make "smelling jars" by dividing the containers into pairs. For each pair, sprinkle a little of the same scent on the cotton balls. Put the lids on the containers.
- Set the smelling jars on a table.

Introducing the Project

Spray a little perfume into the air. Let your children enjoy the fragrance. What sense did they use? Have them tell you about all the other kinds of things they can smell. Then explain the following project steps to the children.

The Project

1. Select one of the smelling jars and smell it.

2. Smell the other jars until you find one with a matching scent.

3. Repeat with the remaining jars until you have found all of the matching scents.

4. Smell each pair of jars again to find out which fragrance you like the best.

Follow-Up

Take your children on a "scent hike." Walk by a cafeteria as lunch is being prepared, smell a flower, sniff the air after a rainfall, and so on. Copy the worksheets on pages 97-99 for your children to complete in class or at home.

Name_____

Circle the things you like to smell.

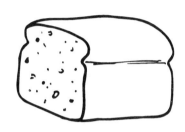

Name_____

Cut out the boxes at the bottom of the page.
Decide what each person in the Smelling family
likes to smell, then glue the boxes in place.

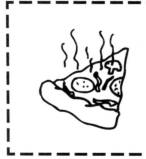

Name_____

Draw something you like to smell.

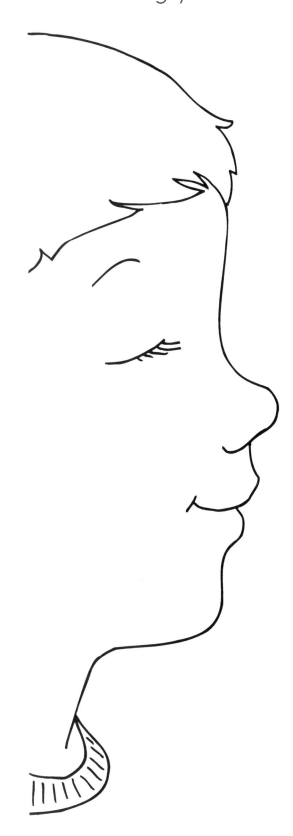

Tasty Treats

Objectives

Explore the sense of taste and complete a chart.

Materials Needed

❑ prepared foods
❑ plates
❑ worksheet
❑ napkins
❑ pencil

Setting Up the Station

• Arrange each of the following foods on a separate plate: soda crackers, apple slices, lemon slices, pretzels, raisins, and pickle slices.

• Copy the Taste This worksheet on page 101.

• Set out the plates of food, copies of the worksheet, napkins, and a pencil.

Introducing the Project

Invite your children to tell you about the things they like to taste. Who likes to taste salty things best? Who likes sweet things best? Tell the children they will be tasting more things, then explain the following project steps.

The Project

1. Take a copy of the worksheet and write your name on it.

2. Place a napkin in front of you and select a piece of each kind of food to put on it.

3. Look at the worksheet. Try the first food listed on it, a cracker. Decide if you like the cracker or not. Put an *X* under the happy face if you like the cracker, or an *X* under the sad face if you do not.

4. Repeat with the other foods.

Follow-Up

Challenge your children to use their sense of taste to identify various foods. Have them close their eyes and hold out their hands. Give each child a small piece of a graham cracker to eat. Could they tell what kind of cracker it was? Next, have them keep their eyes closed as they taste a piece of soda cracker you give them. What kind of cracker was that? Let them think of other taste tests they might want to take. If you wish, copy the worksheets on pages 102-103 for the children to work on in class or at home.

Name_____

Try each food. Put an X under the happy face if
you like it, or an X under the sad face if you do not.

Food	☺	☹
cracker 		
apple 		
lemon 		
pretzel 		
raisin 		
pickle 		

Investigating the Body and the Senses • Investigation Station

Name_____

Draw a line to connect the matching foods.

Name_____

Draw your favorite foods to eat for dinner.

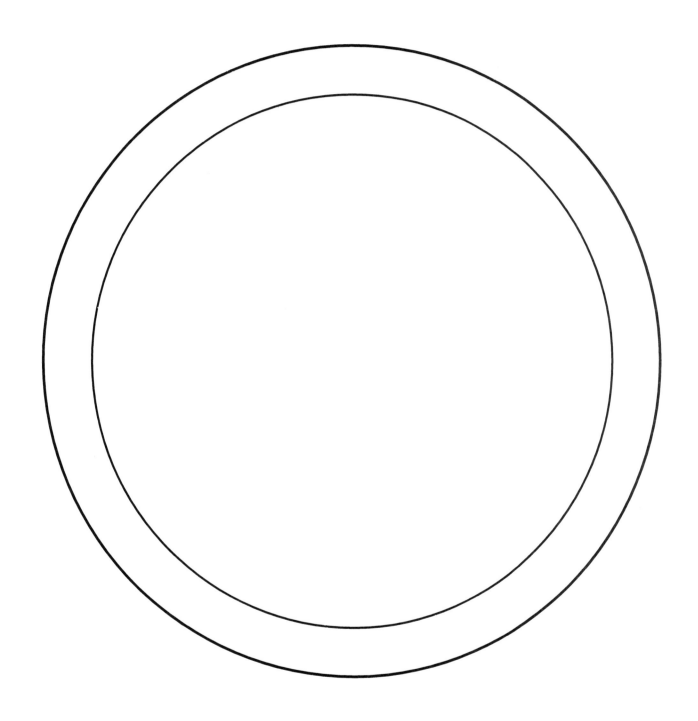

Investigating Magnets and Mirrors

To Stick or Not to Stick

Objectives

Discover what kinds of objects are magnetic.

Materials Needed

❑ household objects
❑ worksheet
❑ magnet
❑ pencil

Setting Up the Station

• Collect the following household objects: a paper clip, a book, a steel nail, a steel washer, a sock, and a wooden block.

• Copy the What's Magnetic? worksheet on page 107.

• Set out the household objects, the copies of the worksheet, a magnet, and a pencil.

Introducing the Project

Show your children the magnet. Ask them to tell you what kinds of things a magnet will stick to. Will it stick to a metal doorknob? Try it out. Will it stick to a plastic chair? Try it out. Test a few more objects, then explain the following project steps to the children.

The Project

1. Take a copy of the worksheet and write your name on it.

2. Look at the first object pictured on the worksheet. Find the object on the table.

3. Hold the magnet to the object. Does the magnet stick to it? If it does, put an *X* by the object in the Magnetic column. If the magnet does not stick to the object, put an *X* by it in the Nonmagnetic column.

4. Continue with the remaining objects.

Follow-Up

Divide your children into pairs or small groups. Give each pair a magnet. Let them explore the room to find things that are magnetic. If you wish, copy the worksheets on pages 108-109 for them to work on in class or at home.

Name_____

Object	 🚫🧲	 🧲
paper clip		
book 		
nail 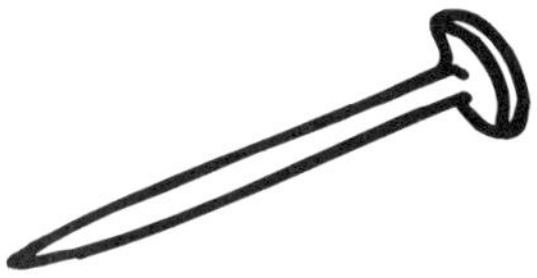		
washer 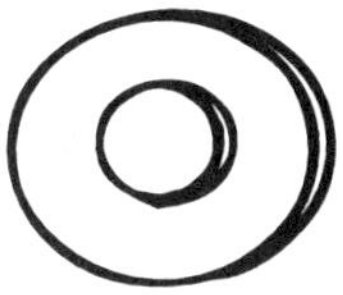		
sock 		
block 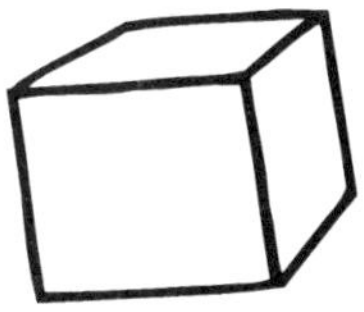		

Name_____

Draw a line from the items that are magnetic to the magnet.

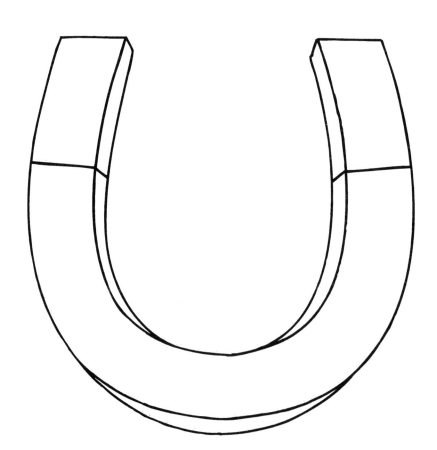

Name_____

Connect the dots to discover a kind of magnet.

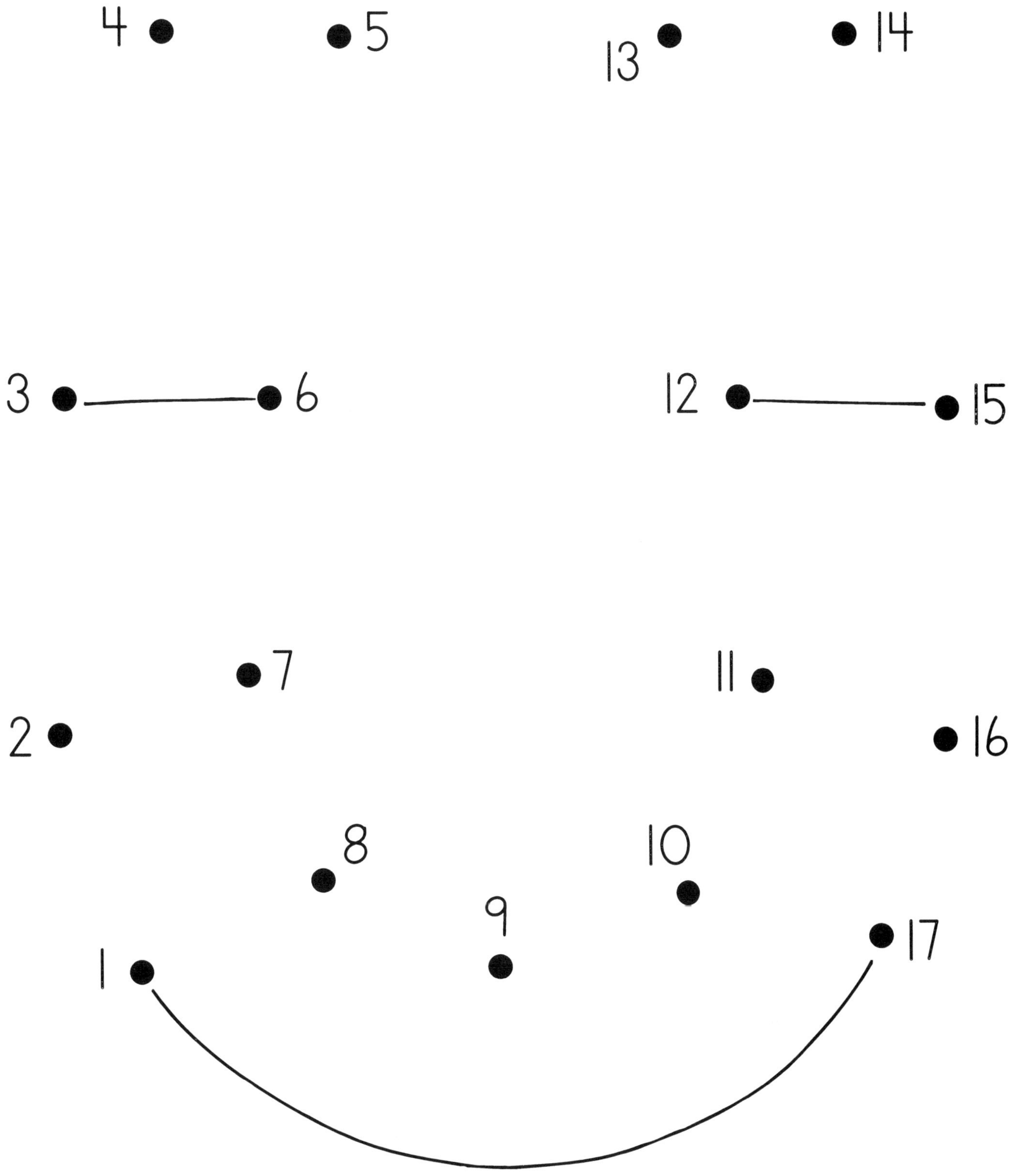

4 •   • 5   13 •   •14

3 •——————• 6   12 •——————• 15

•7   11•

2 •   •16

8•   10•

9•

1•   •17

Magnetic Attraction

Objectives

Learn about how magnets attract and repel one another.

Materials Needed

❏ donut-shaped magnets
❏ dowel
❏ modeling dough

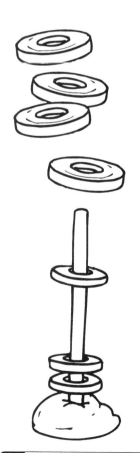

Setting Up the Station

- Collect several donut-shaped magnets. (Check your local school supply store or craft store.)
- Find a 6- to 8-inch dowel. Make sure the magnets can fit over the dowel.
- Make a rounded base with the modeling dough. Place the dowel so it is standing up in the center of the base.
- Set out the dowel base and the magnets.

Introducing the Project

Explain to your children that a magnet has two sides: one side that is a positive ("+") side, and one side that is a negative ("-") side. Tell them that the positive side of one magnet will only stick to the negative side of another magnet. If two positive sides are close, they will actually push (*repel*) the magnets apart. Demonstrate this by holding two magnets together. If they are put together one way, they stick to (*attract*) each other. If they are put together another way, they push themselves apart. Tell the children they will be experimenting with this themselves. Then explain the following project steps.

The Project

1. Select one of the donut-shaped magnets and put it on the dowel.

2. Place another magnet on the dowel. Is it attracted to the first magnet or is it being repelled?

3. Put two or three more magnets on the dowel, observing which magnets are being attracted to each other and which ones are being repelled.

Follow-Up

Give each of your children an index card with a plus sign or a minus sign written on it. Have the children pretend to be magnets and carefully walk around the room, being attracted to "magnets" with the opposite sign and being repelled by "magnets" with the same sign. If you wish, copy the worksheets on pages 111-113 for your children to work on in class or at home.

Name_____

Count the magnets on each dowel. Write
that number on each line.

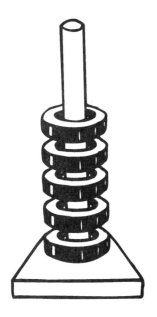

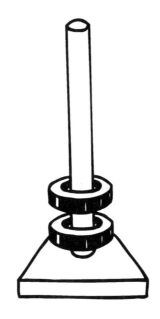

_____

_____

_____

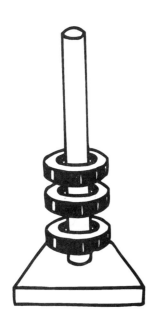

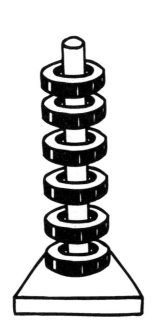

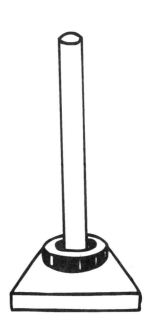

_____

_____

_____

Name_____

Draw a line from each "+" magnet to a "–" magnet.

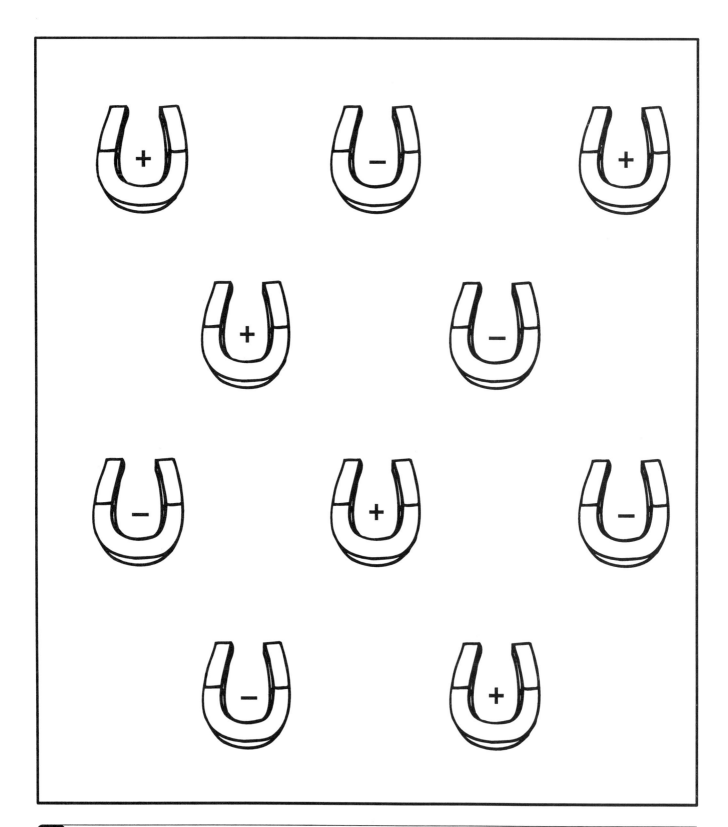

Name_____

Help the magnet in the middle find the way
to the magnet it's attracted to.

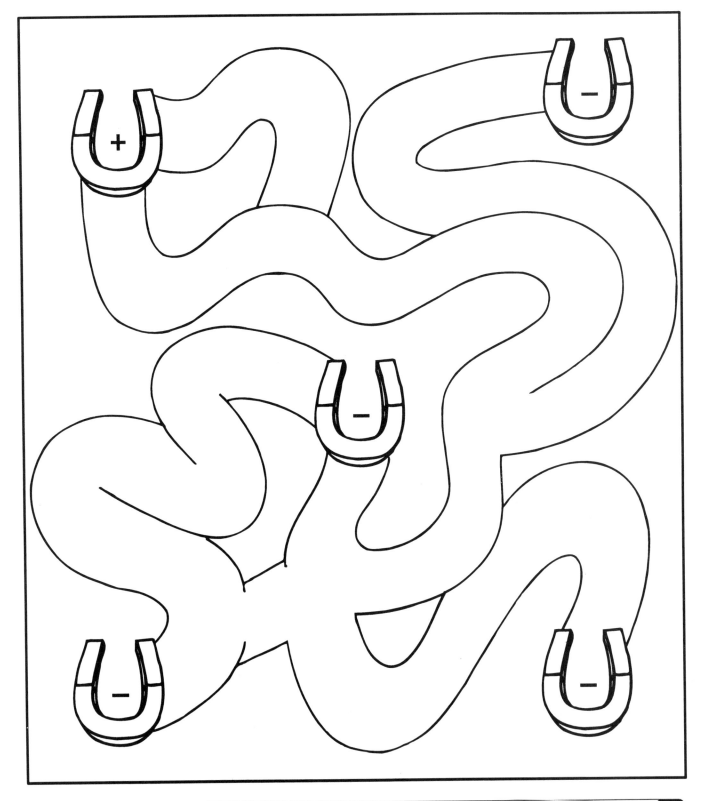

Magnetic Moves

Objective

Observe how a magnet can move another object.

Materials Needed

❏ sturdy box lids
❏ worksheets
❏ scissors
❏ rubber cement
❏ steel washers
❏ strong magnets

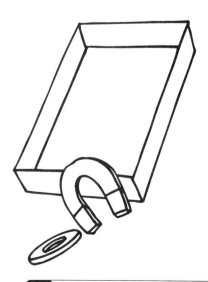

Setting Up the Station

- Find three sturdy box lids, at least 6 inches wide and 8 inches long.
- Make one copy of each of the worksheets on pages 115-117.
- Cut out one of the mazes and rubber-cement it to the top of the lid. Repeat with the other two mazes.
- Find or purchase three steel washers. (Aluminum washers will not work.)
- Find three strong magnets.
- Set out the prepared mazes along with the magnets and washers.

Introducing the Station

Show your children one of the mazes. Show them the magnet and the washer. Place the washer on top of the box lid at the start of the maze. Demonstrate how to move the washer along the maze by moving the magnet underneath the box. Then explain the following project steps to them.

The Project

1. Select one of the mazes. Make sure the washer is at the start line and the magnet is underneath it, under the box lid.
2. Move the magnet carefully along the maze until the washer reaches its destination.
3. Repeat with the remaining mazes.

Follow-Up

Collect cardboard, magnets, and washers for your children. Let them design their own mazes or crazy paths on the cardboard. Have them take turns following each other's mazes with the magnets and washers.

Reflections

Objectives

Observe reflections in a variety of objects.

Materials Needed

❑ mirrors
❑ reflective materials
❑ worksheet
❑ crayons

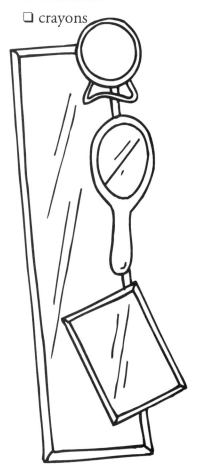

Setting Up the Station

- Collect a variety of mirrors, including at least one hand mirror and a full-length mirror.
- Find an assortment of reflective materials, such as a shiny pot or baking sheet, a piece of aluminum foil, and a metal bowl.
- Copy the In the Mirror worksheet on page 119.
- Set out the mirrors, the reflective materials, the copies of the worksheet, and crayons.

Introducing the Project

Show your children a mirror. What do they see in it? Explain that what they see is a *reflection*, a kind of picture of what is in front of the mirror. Tell them that other things make reflections, too. Hold up one of the reflective materials so the children can see their reflections in it. Then explain the following project steps to them.

The Project

1. Choose one of the mirrors. Look into it. What do you see? What happens when you move? Does your reflection move? Make a funny face. Does your reflection make the same face?

2. Check for your reflection in the other mirrors and reflective items on the table. Which gives you the best reflection?

3. Take a copy of the worksheet. Look into a hand mirror and draw on the worksheet the reflection you see in the mirror—you!

Follow-Up

Give each of your children a metal spoon. Have them look at their reflection on the back and front of the spoons. Have them notice that their reflection changes from thin to wide on the back of the spoon because the spoon makes a *convex* mirror. On the front of the spoon, their reflection is upside down because it is curved like a *concave* mirror. Does the concave side of the spoon reflect everything upside down? (Yes.) If you wish, copy the worksheets on pages120-121 for the children to work on in class or at home.

Name_____

Draw what you see in the mirror.

Name_____

Draw a line to connect the matching mirrors.

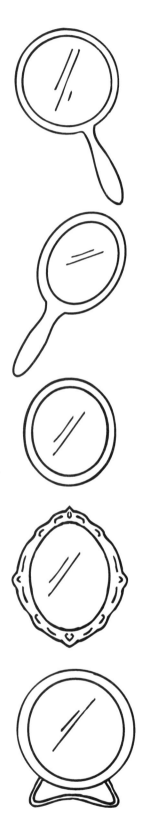

Name_____

Circle the girl's exact reflection.

Mirror Magic

Objectives

Learn about symmetry and solve problems.

Materials Needed

❑ mirror
❑ worksheets
❑ scissors
❑ clear self-stick paper (optional)

Setting Up the Station

• Find or purchase a rectangular, travel-size mirror.
• Make a copy of each of the Half Pattern worksheets on pages 123-124, and cut out the half pictures.
• If you wish, cover the half pictures with clear self-stick paper or have them laminated.
• Set out the travel mirror and the half pictures.

Introducing the Project

Show your children one of the half pictures. Demonstrate how to hold the mirror on the side of the half picture (at right angles) to make a whole picture. Then explain the following project steps.

The Project

1. Select one of the half pictures.

2. Hold the mirror alongside the half picture until you can see the whole picture.

3. Repeat with the remaining half pictures.

Follow-Up

Let the children find magazine pictures to cut in half. Let them take turns using the mirror to turn the half pictures into whole pictures. If you wish, copy the worksheet on page 125 for the children to complete in class or at home.

Name_____

Cut out the squares at the bottom of the page. Glue each square in the appropriate box to make the half pictures whole.

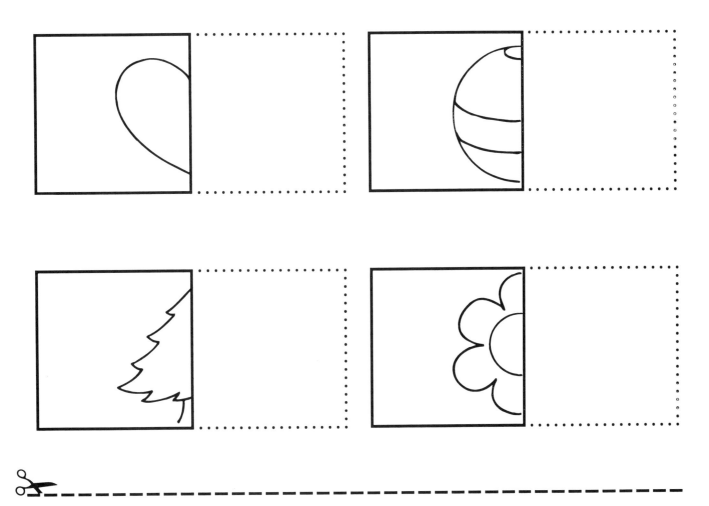

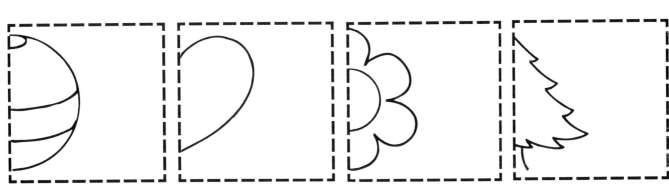

Investigating More Science Fun

Science Jars

Objectives

Observe and experiment.

Materials Needed

- ❑ jars with lids
- ❑ permanent marker
- ❑ fill materials
- ❑ worksheet
- ❑ pencil

Setting Up the Station

- Find six clear-plastic jars with lids (peanut butter jars work well).
- Use a permanent marker to number the jars from 1 to 6.
- Fill each jar at least halfway with a different material, such as sand, cotton balls, feathers, popcorn kernels, rice, dried beans, or craft beads. Put on the lids and secure tightly.
- Copy the List of Jars worksheet on page 129.
- Set out the jars, the copies of the worksheet, and a pencil.

Introducing the Project

Show your children the jars. Hold up one of the jars. Ask the children to help you think of as many words as they can to describe the contents of the jar. Tell them they will be examining the jars closely when they are at the station. Then explain the following project steps, reading the worksheet with them. (You may wish to have an adult helper at this station.)

The Project

1. Look carefully at the jars. Pick up the jars one at a time and shake them. What kind of sounds do they make?

2. Use your hands to "weigh" the jars. Which one seems to weigh the most?

3. Take a copy of the worksheet. Write the number of the jar that best completes each sentence. You can use a number more than once.

Follow-Up

Have the children sit down with their List of Jars worksheets. Help them compare their answers. If you wish, copy the worksheets on pages 130-131 for the children to complete in class or at home.

Name_____

On each blank, fill in the number of the jar that best completes the sentence.

 The heaviest jar is _____.

 The lightest jar is _____.

 The noisiest jar is _____.

 The quietest jar is _____.

 The most colorful jar is ____.

 My favorite jar is _____.

Name_____

For each row, look at the first jar and
circle the jar that matches it exactly.

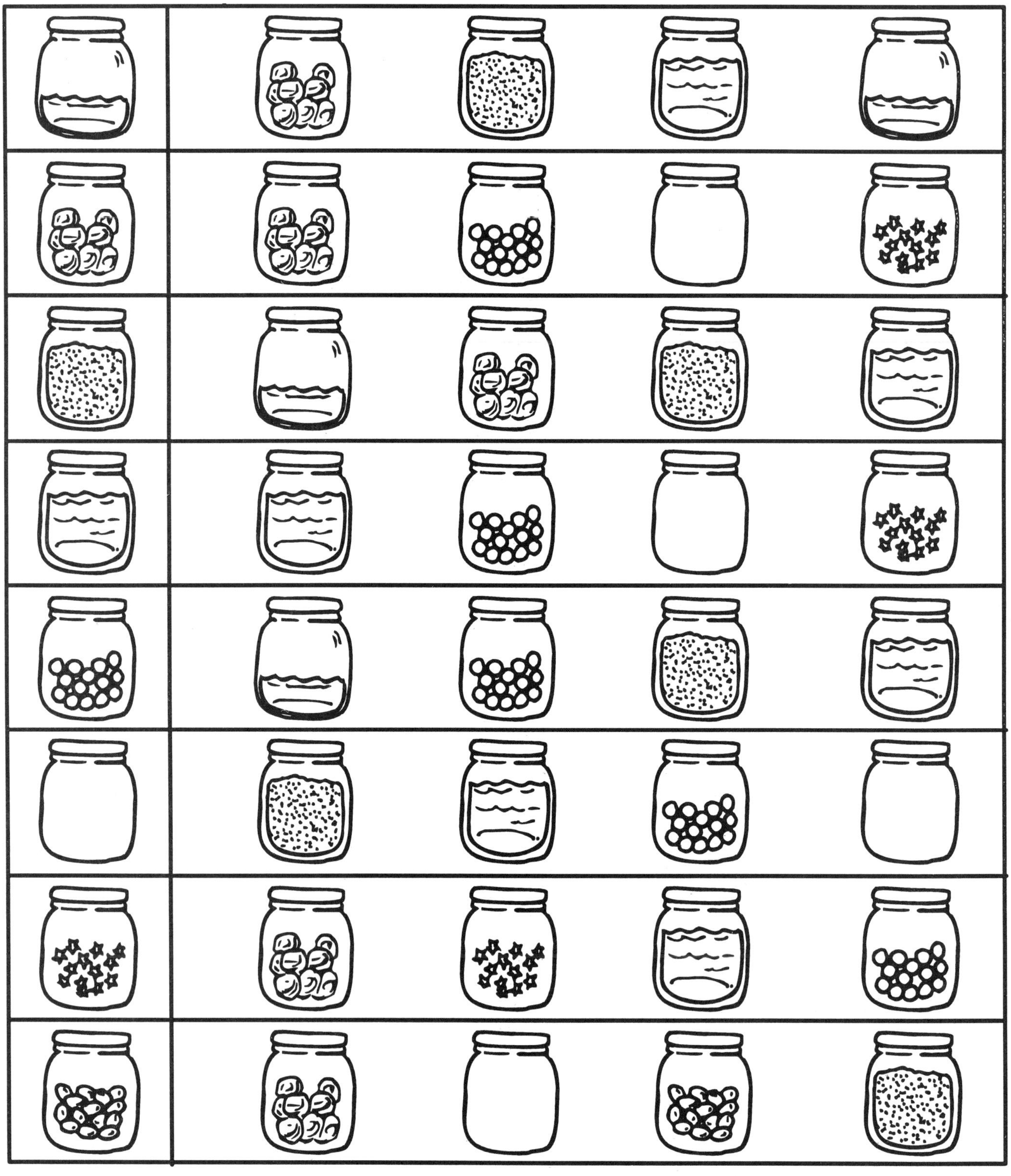

Name_____

Circle the jar that has more.

Circle the jar that has less.

Investigating More Science Fun • Investigation Station

Wheels

Objectives

Learn which shapes make good wheels.

Materials Needed

❑ craft knife
❑ cardboard
❑ unsharpened pencils

Setting Up the Station

- Use a craft knife to cut these shapes out of cardboard: a circle, a square, a triangle, and a rectangle.
- Poke a hole in the center of each shape, large enough for an unsharpened pencil to fit through.
- Set out the cardboard shapes and some unsharpened pencils.

Introducing the Station

Ask your children to tell you what shape they think makes the best wheel. Encourage them to think about the wheels they've seen. What shape are they? Explain the following project steps to the children, in which they will experiment with wheel shapes.

The Project

1. Select one of the cardboard shapes.

2. Gently push the shape onto the middle of one of the pencils.

3. Try to roll the pencil on the table. How does it roll?

4. Try rolling the remaining shapes. Think about which shape rolled the best.

Follow-Up

Ask your children to tell you what shape rolled the best. Why do they think it rolled so well? Let them go on a "wheel search" in your room. Have each child count the number of wheeled objects he or she finds. If you wish, copy the worksheets on pages 133-135 for the children to work on in class or at home.

Name_____

Color the shapes that make the best wheels.

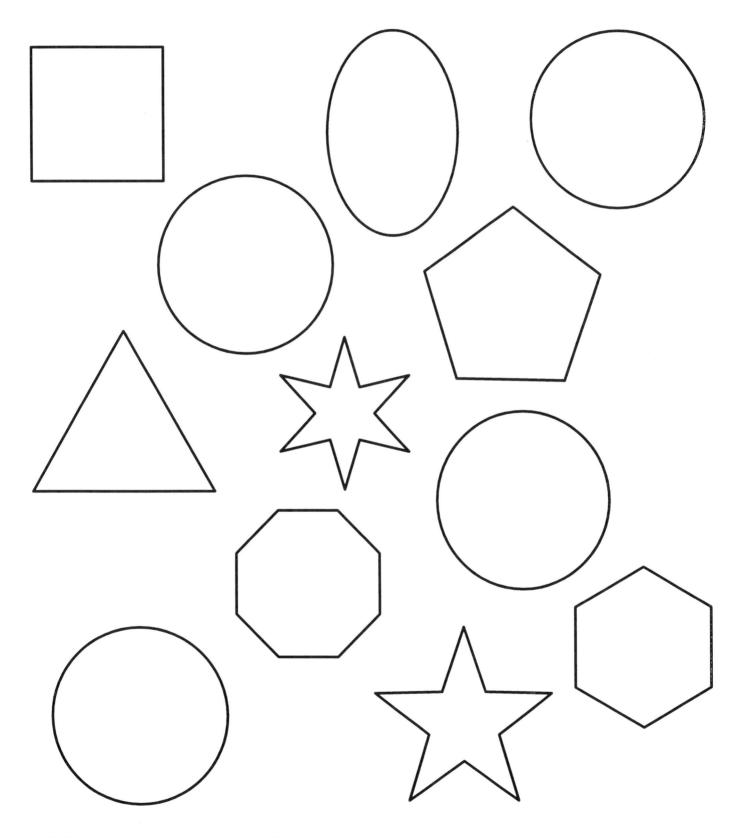

Name_____

For each vehicle, count the wheels and
draw a line to the matching number.

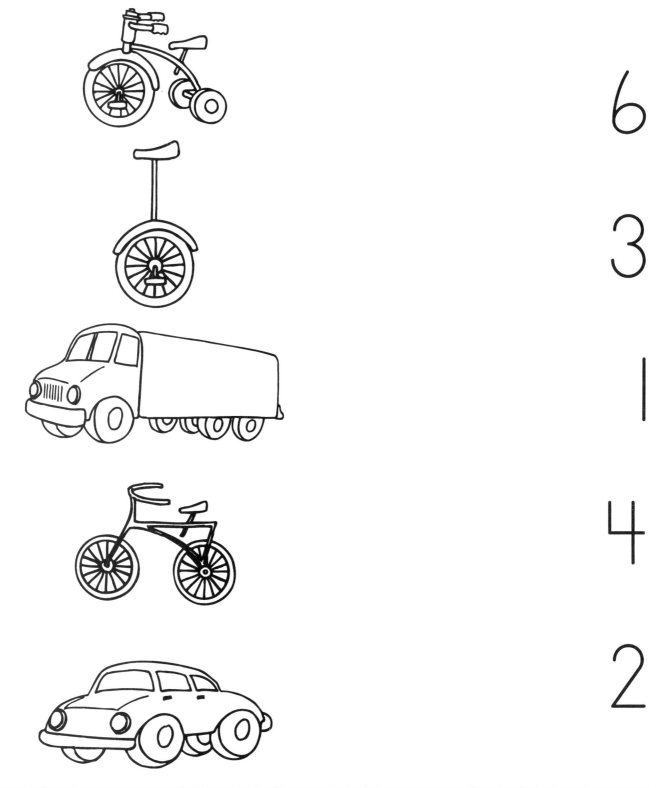

6

3

1

4

2

Name_____

Design your own wheeled vehicle.

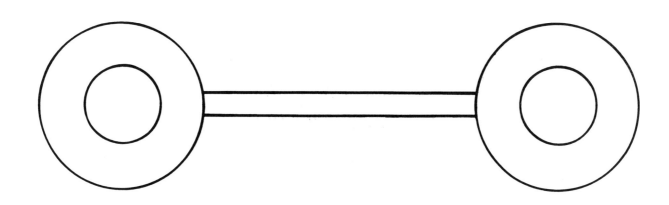

Dinosaur Fossils

Objectives

Learn about dinosaurs and their fossils.

Materials Needed

❑ pictures of fossils
❑ plastic dinosaurs
❑ modeling clay

Setting Up the Station

• Check your library for some pictures of dinosaur fossils.

• Collect or purchase three or four different small plastic dinosaurs.

• Set out the fossil pictures, the plastic dinosaurs, and some modeling clay.

Introducing the Project

Show your children the pictures of dinosaur fossils. Explain that the fossils were made a long time ago out of the bones of the dinosaurs that lived then. Scientists look at the fossils to learn more about the dinosaurs—what they looked like, how big they were, and so on. Tell the children they will be making their own dinosaur "fossils," then explain the following project steps.

The Project

1. Choose one of the plastic dinosaurs.

2. Take a lump of modeling clay and flatten it a little.

3. Press the side of the dinosaur into the clay.

4. Lift out the dinosaur and look at the imprint it made in the clay.

5. Repeat with the other dinosaurs.

6. When you have made all of your "fossils," see if you can match each dinosaur to its own fossil.

Follow-Up

Hang up some pictures of dinosaurs. Learn the names of the dinosaurs along with your children. If you wish, copy the worksheets on pages 137-139 for your children to work on in class or at home.

Name_____

Draw a line connecting each fossil to its dinosaur.

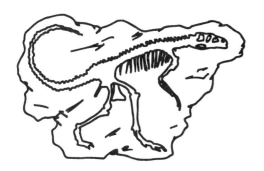

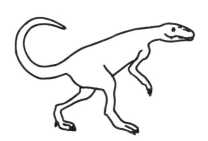

Name_____

Help the scientist discover what dinosaur
he has found by connecting the dots.

Name_____

Find the dinosaurs hidden in the swamp. Color them.

As Big As

Objectives

Practice measuring.

Materials Needed

☐ household objects
☐ scissors
☐ tagboard

Setting Up the Station

- Collect five or six household objects of varying lengths, such as a shoe, a craft stick, a baking sheet, a toy truck, and a book.
- Cut tagboard into strips that are the same length as the objects.
- Set out the objects and the paper strips.

Introducing the Project

Talk with your children about measuring things. Can anyone find something that is the same length as their arm? As their foot? Tell them there are lots of different ways to measure things. Then explain the following project steps.

The Project

1. Select one of the paper strips.

2. Hold the strip alongside one of the objects. Is it the same length? If it is, go on to the next paper strip. If it is not, keep searching until you have found the object that is the same length.

3. Continue with the remaining paper strips.

Follow-Up

Divide your children into pairs. Give each pair of children a ruler. Show them how to use the ruler to measure things, then let them take turns measuring small things around the room. If you wish, copy the worksheets on pages 141-143 for your children to work on in class or at home.

Name_____

Circle the pairs that are the same length.

Name_____

Write the number of inches long that each item is.

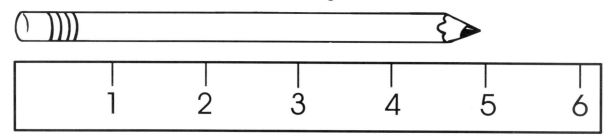

_____ inches

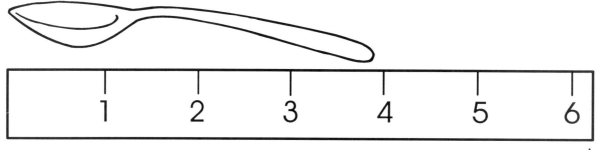

_____ inches

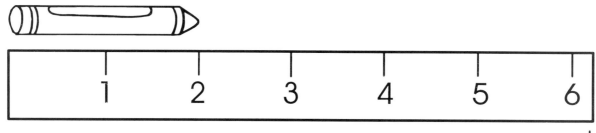

_____ inches

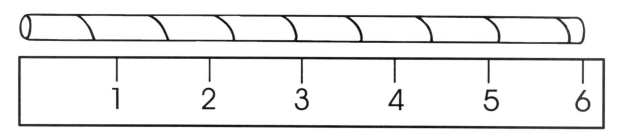

_____ inches

Name_____

Draw something as big as this tree.

Shadow Explorations

Objectives

Learn about shadows and how to make them.

Materials Needed

- ❑ white butcher paper
- ❑ bright light
- ❑ solid objects
- ❑ worksheet
- ❑ pencil

Setting Up the Station

- Cover a table with white butcher paper.
- Set up a bright light to shine on the table. A lamp with its shade removed works well; so does an adjustable shop light that you can clamp to the table or a chair.
- Collect several solid, opaque objects such as a block, a small book, a spoon, a toy car, and a leaf.
- Copy the Make a Shadow worksheet on page 145.
- Set out the objects, the copies of the worksheet, and a pencil.

Introducing the Project

Ask your children if they know how a shadow is made. What do they need to make a shadow? (Light.) Hold up the bright light. Show them how to make a shadow by standing in front of the light. Let your children figure out where to stand in order to make a shadow on the wall. Then explain the following project steps.

The Project

1. Select one of the objects.

2. Hold the object in front of the light so that it makes a shadow on the paper on the table.

3. Experiment with making the shadow bigger and smaller.

4. Take a copy of the worksheet and write your name on it. Place the worksheet on the table. Hold an object so its shadow falls on the worksheet. Trace around the shadow on the worksheet. Make other shadows to trace around on the worksheet, if you wish.

Follow-Up

Shine the bright light onto a wall. Have your children take turns standing between the light and the wall, to make their shadow fall on the wall. How can they make their shadow move? If you wish, copy the worksheets on pages 146-147 for the children to work on in class or at home.

Name_____

Make a shadow on this paper. Trace around it.

Name_____

Draw a line connecting each shadow
to the object that made it.

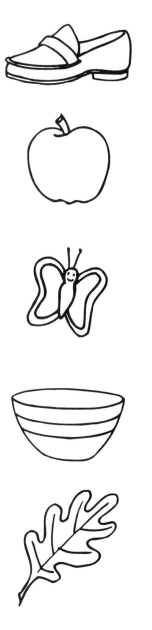

Name_____

Help the girl find her shadow.

Shiny Pennies

Objectives

Observe and follow an experiment.

Materials Needed

❏ dull pennies
❏ vinegar
❏ jars
❏ eyedropper
❏ salt shaker
❏ salt
❏ bowl
❏ spoon
❏ paper towels
❏ shiny penny

Setting Up the Station

- Collect at least two or three dull, tarnished pennies for each child.
- Pour vinegar into a jar and put an eyedropper in it.
- Fill a salt shaker with salt.
- Set out the vinegar, salt, a bowl, a spoon, some paper towels, a jar for collecting the clean pennies, and a shiny penny.

Introducing the Project

Show your children a dull penny and a shiny penny. Tell them you know a special way to make the dull penny shiny again. Then explain the following project steps to them.

The Project

1. Put two or three pennies in the bowl.

2. Use the eyedropper to carefully drop enough vinegar on them to cover them completely. Notice what is happening. (Nothing.)

3. Sprinkle some salt on the pennies. Now what is happening?

4. Gently stir the pennies with the spoon so that all the surfaces are cleaned.

5. Take out the pennies and dry them on a paper towel.

6. Put the clean pennies in the penny jar.

Follow-Up

Collect all the shiny pennies and pour them out in front of the children. Let them help you count the pennies. If you wish, copy the worksheets on pages 149-151 for the children to work on in class or at home.

Name_____

Count each pile of pennies. Draw a line to connect the pennies to the matching number.

1 2 3

0 1 2

3 4 5

4 5 6

2 3 4

3 4 5

Name_____

Draw the correct number of pennies in each coin purse.

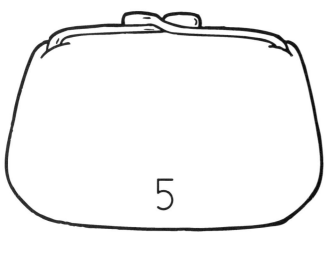

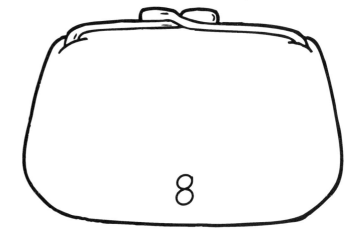

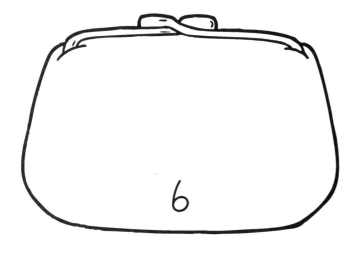

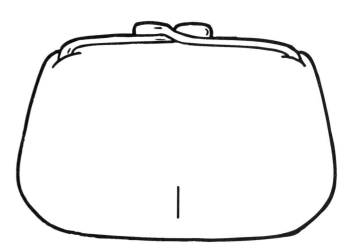

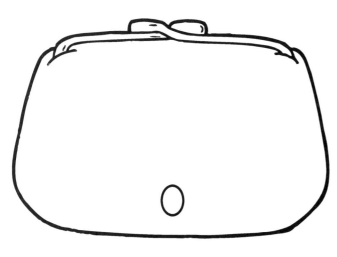

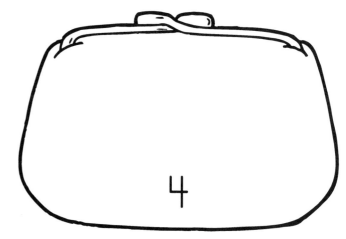

Name_____

Find the six hidden pennies. Color them.

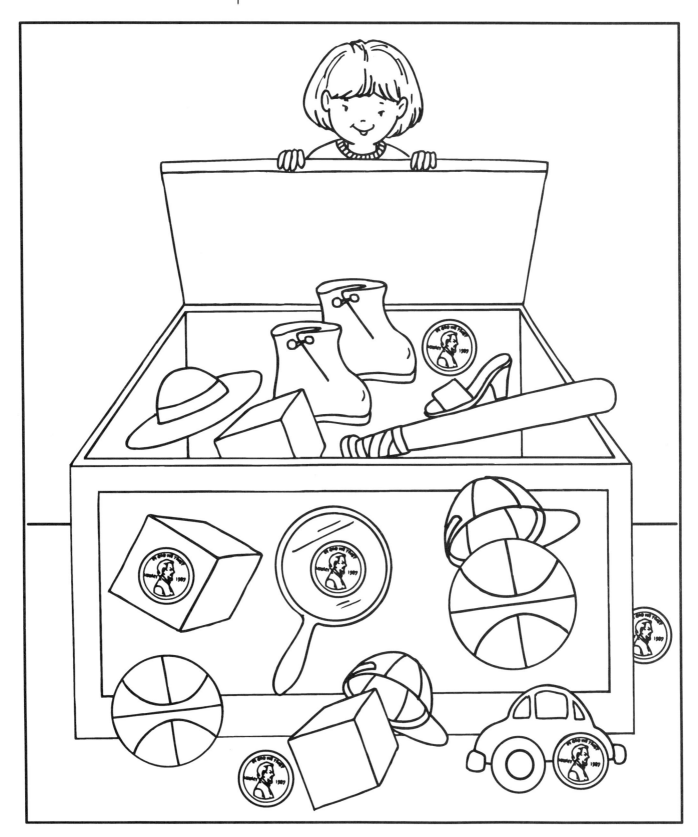

Magic Colors

Objectives

Observe and predict what will happen.

Materials Needed

❏ colored cellophane
❏ scissors
❏ ruler
❏ felt tip markers
❏ white paper

Setting Up the Station

• Collect red and blue colors of cellophane wrap (available where gift-wrap is sold).

• Cut an 8-inch square out of each color of cellophane.

• Use a red felt tip marker to draw a simple shape, such as a star, on a sheet of white paper. Add other, distracting lines with a blue felt tip marker. Repeat on a second sheet of paper, using blue for the shape and red for the distracting lines.

• Set out the papers, the cellophane squares, more white paper, and the red and blue felt tip markers.

Introducing the Project

Hold up one of the cellophane squares so your children can see through it. What do they see? Tell them they will have a chance to experiment with these magic color squares. Then explain the following project steps.

The Project

1. Choose one of the red and blue papers. Put the red cellophane square over it. What do you see? (Just the blue lines are visible; the red lines disappear when viewed through the red cellophane.)

2. Pick up the blue cellophane square. Guess what you'll see when you put it over the papers. (Just the red lines.) Put the blue cellophane over the paper to find out if you guessed correctly.

3. Use the red and blue felt tip markers to create your own designs on the plain white paper. Look at them through the red and blue cellophane squares.

Follow-Up

Cut a small piece of red or blue cellophane for each of your children. Lead them on a color hike as they look at the world through their magic color square. If you wish, copy the worksheets on pages 153-155 for the children to work on in class or at home.

Name_____

For each row, color the two shapes that match.

Name_____

Color the picture. ◯=red ☐=blue
△=yellow ☆=green

Name_____

For each row, identify the number and
color that many items.

2	♡ ♡ ♡ ♡ ♡ ♡
5	☆ ☆ ☆ ☆ ☆ ☆
1	◇ ◇ ◇ ◇ ◇ ◇
4	🌷 🌷 🌷 🌷 🌷 🌷
3	▢ ▢ ▢ ▢ ▢ ▢
6	🦋 🦋 🦋 🦋 🦋 🦋

Classification Fun

Objectives

Identify attributes and classify objects.

Materials Needed

❏ household objects
❏ tray
❏ set of colorful blocks

Setting Up the Station

• Collect a variety of household objects that could be sorted in a variety of ways (color, size, purpose, texture, etc.).

• Place the items on a tray and set them out on a table.

Introducing the Project

Talk with your children about grouping or classifying objects. Show your children a set of colorful blocks. Let them help you sort them by color. Challenge the children to think of another way to sort them by (size or shape). Then explain the following project steps.

The Project

1. Look at the objects on the tray. Think of a way to sort them.

2. Sort the objects in that way.

3. Put the objects back on the tray and think of another way to sort them.

4. Sort the objects in the second way.

5. Repeat as many times as you can.

Follow-Up

Play a classifying game with your children. Have them think of ways to group themselves, such as by kind of shoe, shirt or sock color, favorite food, or number of buttons on their clothes. Try as many different groupings as you would like. If you wish, copy the worksheets on pages 157-159 for the children to work on in class or at home.

Name_____

Color the △ purple.
Color the ☐ orange.

Name_____

Draw lines to connect each size of object to the matching size of bear.

Name_____

Cut out the squares at the bottom of the worksheet.
For each box, glue the matching object in it.

Totline Publications

Teacher Books

BEST OF TOTLINE® SERIES
Totline Magazine's best ideas.
Best of Totline
Best of Totline Parent Flyers

BUSY BEES SERIES
Seasonal ideas for twos and threes.
Busy Bees—Fall
Busy Bees—Winter
Busy Bees—Spring
Busy Bees—Summer

CELEBRATIONS SERIES
Early learning through celebrations.
Small World Celebrations
Special Day Celebrations
Great Big Holiday Celebrations
Celebrating Likes and Differences

EXPLORING SERIES
Versatile, hands-on learning.
Exploring Sand
Exploring Water
Exploring Wood

FOUR SEASONS
Active learning through the year.
Four Seasons—Art
Four Seasons—Math
Four Seasons—Movement
Four Seasons—Science

GREAT BIG THEMES SERIES
Giant units designed around a theme.
Space • Zoo • Circus

KINDERSTATION SERIES
Learning centers for learning with language, art, and math.
Calculation Station
Communication Station
Creation Station
Investigation Station

LEARNING & CARING ABOUT
Teach children about their world.
Our World • Our Town

MIX & MATCH PATTERNS
Simple patterns to save time!
Animal Patterns
Everyday Patterns
Holiday Patterns
Nature Patterns

1•2•3 SERIES
Open-ended learning.
1•2•3 Art
1•2•3 Blocks
1•2•3 Games
1•2•3 Colors
1•2•3 Puppets
1•2•3 Reading & Writing
1•2•3 Rhymes, Stories & Songs
1•2•3 Math
1•2•3 Science
1•2•3 Shapes

1001 SERIES
Super reference books.
1001 Teaching Props
1001 Teaching Tips
1001 Rhymes & Fingerplays

PIGGYBACK® SONG BOOKS
New lyrics sung to the tunes of childhood favorites!
Piggyback Songs
More Piggyback Songs
Piggyback Songs for Infants and Toddlers
Holiday Piggyback Songs
Animal Piggyback Songs
Piggyback Songs for School
Piggyback Songs to Sign
Spanish Piggyback Songs
More Piggyback Songs for School

PROBLEM SOLVING SAFARI
Teaching problem solving skills.
Problem Solving—Art
Problem Solving—Blocks
Problem Solving—Dramatic Play
Problem Solving—Manipulatives
Problem Solving—Outdoors
Problem Solving—Science

REPRODUCIBLE RHYMES
Make-and-take books for emergent readers.
Alphabet Rhymes
Object Rhymes

SNACKS SERIES
Nutrition combines with learning.
Super Snacks • Healthy Snacks
Teaching Snacks • Multicultural Snacks

TERRIFIC TIPS
Handy resources full of valuable tips.
Terrific Tips for Directors
Terrific Tips for Toddler Teachers
Terrific Tips for Preschool Teachers

THEME-A-SAURUS® SERIES
Classroom-tested, instant themes.
Theme-A-Saurus
Theme-A-Saurus II
Toddler Theme-A-Saurus
Alphabet Theme-A-Saurus
Nursery Rhyme Theme-A-Saurus
Storytime Theme-A-Saurus
Multisensory Theme-A-Saurus

TODDLER SERIES
Great for working with 18 mos–3 yrs.
Playtime Props for Toddlers
Toddler Art

Tot-Mobiles
Unique sets of die-cut mobiles for punching out and easy assembly.
Animals & Toys
Beginning Concepts
Four Seasons

Puzzles & Posters

PUZZLES
Kids Celebrate the Alphabet
Kids Celebrate Numbers
African Adventure
Underwater Adventure
Bear Hugs 4-in-1 Puzzle Set
Busy Bees 4-in-1 Puzzle Set

POSTERS
We Work and Play Together
Bear Hugs Health Posters
Busy Bees Area Posters
Reminder Posters

Parent Books

A YEAR OF FUN SERIES
Age-specific books for parenting.
Just for Babies
Just for Ones
Just for Twos
Just for Threes
Just for Fours
Just for Fives

BEGINNING FUN WITH ART
Introduce your child to art fun.
Craft Sticks • Crayons • Felt
Glue • Paint • Paper Shapes
Modeling Dough • Tissue Paper
Scissors • Rubber Stamps
Stickers • Yarn

BEGINNING FUN WITH SCIENCE
Spark your child's interest in science.
Bugs & Butterflies • Plants & Flowers
Magnets • Rainbows & Colors
Sand & Shells • Water & Bubbles

KIDS CELEBRATE SERIES
Delightful stories with related activity ideas, snacks, and songs.
Kids Celebrate the Alphabet
Kids Celebrate Numbers

LEARN WITH PIGGYBACK® SONGS
Captivating music with age-appropriate themes help children learn.
Songs & Games for Babies
Songs & Games for Toddlers
Songs & Games for Threes
Songs & Games for Fours
Sing a Song of Letters
Sing a Song of Animals
Sing a Song of Colors
Sing a Song of Holidays
Sing a Song of Me
Sing a Song of Nature
Sing a Song of Numbers

LEARN WITH STICKERS
Beginning workbook and first reader with 100-plus stickers.
Balloons • Birds • Bows • Bugs
Butterflies • Buttons • Eggs • Flags
Flowers • Hearts • Leaves • Mittens

LEARNING EVERYWHERE
Discover teaching opportunities everywhere you go.
Teaching House
Teaching Trips
Teaching Town

PLAY AND LEARN
Activities for learning through play the Totline way.
Blocks • Instruments • Kitchen
Gadgets • Paper • Puppets • Puzzles

SEEDS FOR SUCCESS
Ideas to help children develop essential life skills for future success.
Growing Creative Kids
Growing Happy Kids
Growing Responsible Kids
Growing Thinking Kids

TIME TO LEARN
Ideas for hands-on learning.
Colors • Letters • Measuring
Numbers • Science • Shapes
Matching and Sorting • New Words
Cutting and Pasting
Drawing and Writing • Listening
Taking Care of Myself

Puppet Pals
These instant puppets fit on craft sticks, pencils or straws for language props, rewards, and more!
Children's Favorites • The Three Bears
Nursery Rhymes • Old MacDonald
More Nursery Rhymes • Three Little
Pigs • Three Billy Goats Gruff
Little Red Riding Hood